BAY AREA
BioTech
The Future of Life Sciences

SAN FRANCISCO CHAMBER OF COMMERCE
and
MARCOA PUBLISHING, INC.
2004

**SAN FRANCISCO
CHAMBER OF COMMERCE**
Where smart business starts.

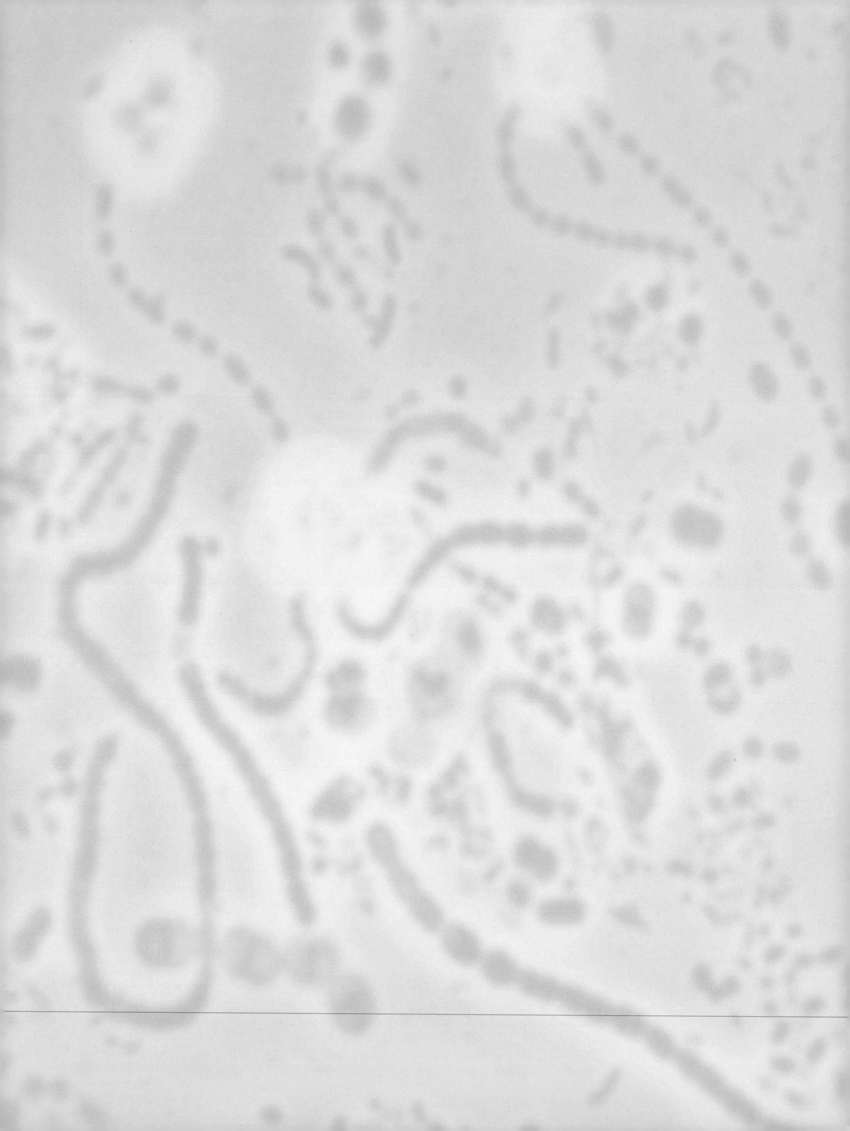

BAY AREA

BIOTECH

The Future of Life Sciences

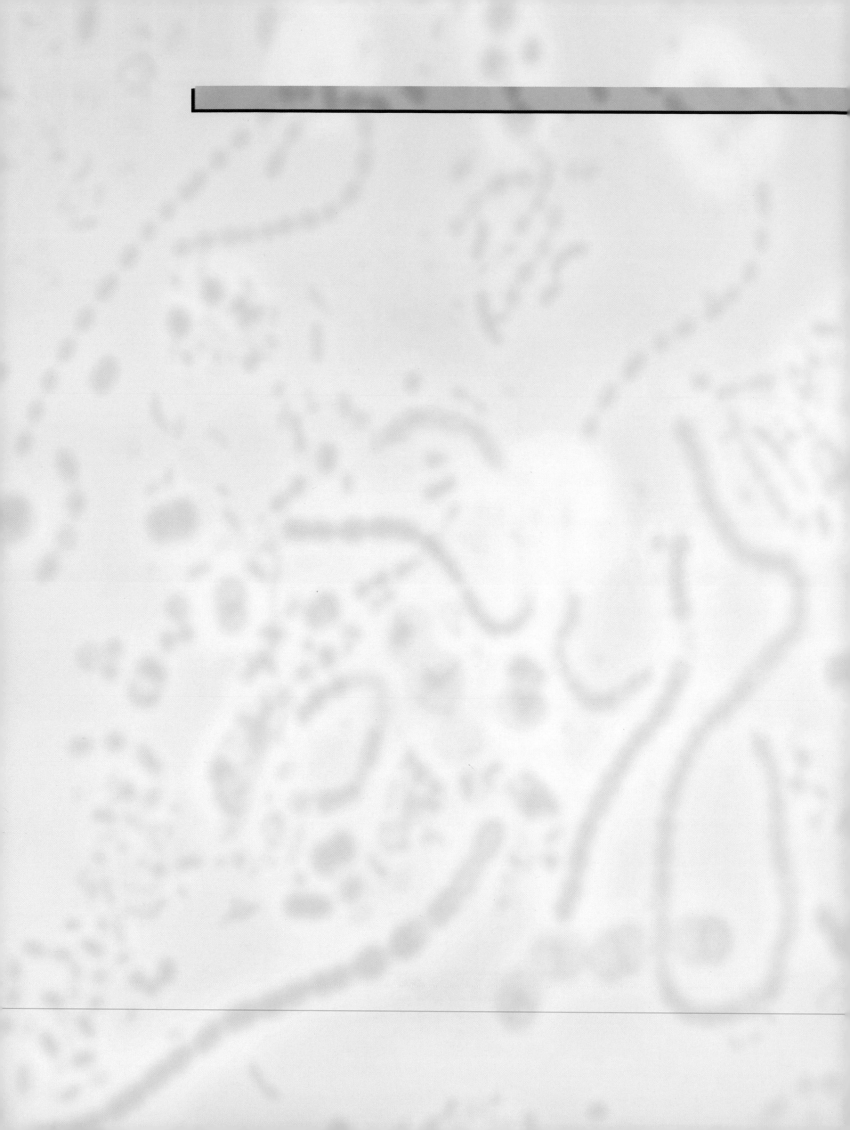

Feature Writers

Bay Area Bioscience Center (BayBio)
was founded in 1990 by a consortium of universities, public officials, educators and bioscience executives to foster a regional climate in which bioscience may continue to flourish. BayBio is an independent, nonprofit organization that works to keep Northern California in the forefront of bioscience activity. Pictured here is Caitlyn Waller, acting presisent, BayBio.

G. Steven Burrill
is CEO of Burrill & Company, a San Francisco-based life-sciences merchant bank. Burrill & Company's business revolves around three core activities: venture-capital investment, strategic partnering and BioStreet™. He is chair of the boards of Pyxis Genomics and Paradigm Genetics. Prior to founding Burrill & Company in 1994, he spent 28 years with Ernst & Young, directing and coordinating the firm's services to clients in the biotechnology/life-sciences/high-technology/manufacturing industries. As an internationally recognized spokesperson for the life-sciences and high-technology industries, Burrill has authored a variety of articles and books, including his most recent industry report, *Biotech 2002: Life Sciences—Systems Biology*. Burrill founded the Foundation for the National Medals of Science and Technology and currently serves on its board of directors.

DPR Construction Inc.
is a forward-thinking, general contactor and construction company that specializes in technically challenging and sustainable projects. DPR Construction has been "building great things" in the Bay Area since 1990. The privately held, employee-owned company is one of the nation's leading biotech builders. Pictured left-to-right is DPR Construction's management team: Sandra Waechter, Jim Dolen, Doug Woods, Peter Nosler, Ron Davidowski, Eric Lamb and Peter Salvati.

Jean Deleage
began his venture-capital career in 1971 in Paris with Sofinnova and, in 1976, started its very successful American subsidiary, Sofinnova Inc., located in San Francisco. In 1979, he formed Burr, Egan, Deleage & Co. (BEDCO) with Craig Burr and William Egan. During the 1980s and 1990s, BEDCO was a prominent, diversified venture firm. He co-founded Alta Partners in 1996. Deleage is an industry leader in biotechnology and has invested in some leading biotechnology companies, such as Genentech, Chiron and Cephalon. Jean holds a Masters Degree in Electrical Engineering from the École Supérieure d'Electricité and a Philosophie Doctorate in Economics from the Sorbonne. In 1993, Jean was awarded the Legion of Honor by the French government in recognition of his career accomplishments.

Frederick Dorey
is special counsel in the Life Sciences Group of Cooley Godward LLP, a national law firm specializing in technology and high-growth companies. Dorey counsels biotechnology, instrumentation and technology companies regarding formation, licensing and strategic partnering. He also advises foundations, research institutes and universities about licensing and commercialization activities. Prior to joining Cooley Godward, Dorey was the first president of the Bay Area Bioscience Center (BayBio). He is a director of the American Liver Foundation, BayBio and the World Affairs Council of Northern California.

Roopa Ghirnikar
is currently the scientific writer at Genencor International Inc. Before joining Genencor, she was a research associate at Stanford University. She received her Philosophie Doctorate in Biochemistry from Virginia Commonwealth University.

Mike Hildreth

, partner, leads Ernst & Young's America's Life Sciences practice in the United States. Hildreth is responsible for developing go-to-market strategies and relationship-development processes for the life-sciences industry. He has practiced public accounting for more than 23 years, the last 20 of which have been with Ernst & Young. Hildreth is a recognized leader in assisting companies with strategic alliances, as well as public and private equity offerings. He is a frequent speaker on emerging industry, SEC and growth-company issues and is a guest lecturer in the venture-capital program at Stanford University and UC Berkeley's Haas School of Business. Hildreth co-developed the firm's IPO Transformation process and is a contributing editor for Ernst & Young's annual biotechnology report. Hildreth is a member of the American Institute of Certified Public Accountants and the California Society of Certified Public Accountants. He is a graduate of Stanford University.

Michael W. Hunkapiller
became president of Applied Biosystems in 1998. He was elected senior vice president of Perkin-Elmer (PE), now Applera Corp., in 1997 and also became president of PE's Applied Biosystems Division at that time. Hunkapiller pioneered the development of automated systems for the analysis, synthesis and purification of proteins, peptides and nucleic acids. He has 24 issued US patents and numerous foreign counterparts covering these instruments and their associated chemistries. In 2001, Hunkapiller received the first annual Takeda Award for Techno-Entrepreneurial Achievement for Individual/Humanity Well-Being for his contribution to the development of automated high-throughput DNA sequencers and the promotion of the foundation of Celera Genomics.

In 1970, Hunkapiller received a Bachelor of Science in Chemistry from Oklahoma Baptist University and, in 1974, a Philosophie Doctorate in Chemical Biology from the California Institute of Technology.

Feature Writers

Kenneth E. Jenkins

is an associate at Townsend and Townsend and Crew LLP, whose practice focuses on patent prosecution, primarily in the biotechnology and pharmaceutical industries. He has written and prosecuted patents relating to a variety of technologies, including combinatorial chemistry, nucleic acid chemistry, high throughput screening, protein chemistry and small-molecule inhibition. Jenkins received his Juris Doctorate degree at University of California, Hastings College of the Law in 2002.

Greg Jensen

, an analyst with Ernst & Young's Life Science Industry Group, has more than eight years of experience in the biotechnology industry. Jensen has primarily worked with early-stage life-sciences companies, providing services such as advice on business plans, market-scoping studies, investor presentations and identifying business-development opportunities. Jensen serves on the sponsorship committee of the Biotechnology Industry Organization and has a Bachelors of Science in Biology and Chemistry from the University of Utah. He also completed an internship at the Rockefeller Institute in New York City.

Christopher Keenan

is responsible for corporate communications at Aradigm Corp., a leader in needle-free drug-delivery systems based in Hayward. With more than 10 years of experience in scientific communications, his work has encompassed involvement with several small-to-mid-sized emerging biotechnology companies, as well as a *Fortune* 500 high-technology company. He received his Bachelors of Arts in English from Kenyon College.

Jeffry S. Mann

, an associate at Townsend and Townsend and Crew LLP, focuses on patent strategy and prosecution, primarily in organic and organometallic chemistry, materials, pharmaceuticals, spectroscopy, separations, catalysis and biotechnology. Mann also has extensive experience in performing reviews, assessing his clients' freedom to enter a technological area and obtaining patent protection for their inventions.

Before entering the field of law, Mann was an assistant professor in the Department of Radiology at the University of California, San Francisco (UCSF) where he was director of chemical research at the Contrast Media Laboratory. He was also a postdoctoral fellow in the Department of Pharmacy at UCSF. Mann received his Juris Doctorate from Golden Gate University in 1997.

Laura T. Mazolla

has more than 12 years of experience in the biotechnology industry, from fundamental research and technology development to the commercialization of integrated-instrumentation platforms. She is CEO of Excellin Life Sciences, a start-up with enabling technologies for systems biology. She founded and chairs the NanoBioConvergence organization. Mazzola was an early employee at Affymax and Affymetrix, developing the high-density array technology that became the prototype for the revolutionary GeneChip™ product line. More recently, she helped reorient business development at Symyx Technologies toward the life sciences through collaborations with Merck and Eli Lilly and licensed their first commercial product, which won the Frost & Sullivan 2002 Market Engineering Technology Innovation Award. Mazzola received a Bachelors of Science from Kalamazoo College and a Masters of Science and Philosophie Doctorate from Stanford University.

Kathryn J. Mengerink

is an associate at Townsend and Townsend and Crew LLP. Mengerink's practice focuses on patent prosecution and litigation primarily in the fields of biotechnology and chemistry. In 2002, Mengerink received her Philosophie Doctorate in Marine Biology at Scripps Institution of Oceanography, University of California, San Diego.

Sandra J. Miller

of Biodesign Network (BDN) brings nearly 20 years of experience in working with pioneering medical-device physician-inventors and entrepreneurs to her current position as executive director of BDN. Miller's focus with BDN is to develop biomedical-technology-innovation educational programs and resources, particularly in the areas of technology transfer and entrepreneurship. Miller is a liaison for the Stanford Biodesign Program to Stanford's Office of Technology Licensing (OTL) and facilitates the efforts of Stanford faculty and student inventors developing medical technologies. Miller is a member of the Association of University Technology Managers and is a founding member of the Stanford Entrepreneurship Network, whose mission is to support entrepreneurship education, research and collaboration campuswide.

She has produced physician education video series on revolutionary interventional cardiology innovations, such as intravascular ultrasound and directional coronary atherectomy. Miller holds an Masters of Business Administration from Pepperdine University.

Scott Morrison is a partner in the Palo Alto office of Ernst & Young and is the US Life Sciences Leader for Ernst & Young. With 22 years of experience in life sciences, he has worked with companies in the Bay Area and nationally since 1980. Morrison's expertise includes corporate-alliances spinouts, equity carve outs, joint ventures, and mergers and acquisitions. He is co-author of Ernst & Young's 12th – 15th *Biotechnology Industry Annual Reports* and is a frequent speaker on industry matters.

Morrison holds a Bachelors of Science from the University of California, Berkeley, is a board member and former chair of the Bay Area Bioscience Center, a founding board member of the Biotechnology Institute and a board member of BIO's Emerging Company Section.

Cynthia Robbins-Roth is the founder of Bio Venture

Publishing Inc. and BioVenture Consultants. Robbins-Roth has been part of the biotechnology industry since 1981. A frequent speaker on issues and events affecting the industry, she combines a technical background with extensive experience in business and finance issues.

Robbins-Roth holds a Philosophie Doctorate in Biochemistry from the University of Texas Medical Branch, completed post-doctoral work in its Microbiology Department and was a research scientist within the Immunology and Protein Biochemistry groups at Genentech Inc. She then joined the Business Development group at California Biotechnology Inc.

Robbins-Roth has been a consultant to the bioscience industry since 1986, providing technology assessment, competitor analysis, strategic planning, due diligence, market analysis and fund-management consultation services. Robbins-Roth served as a member of the board of directors of NewBiotics and serves on the scientific advisory boards of Genesys Capital (Toronto) and BioVeda Capital (Singapore). Her second book, *From Alchemy to IPO: The Business of Biotechnology*, was published in 2000.

The editors of *Bay Area Biotech* wish to thank the following for their invaluable contributions to creating the publication: Burrill & Company, San Francisco Center for Economic Development, Ernst & Young, Stanford University, Littlehales & Company, PricewaterhouseCoopers, Ginny Milo, University of California, Berkeley, University of California, San Francisco, and the Bay Area Bioscience Center.

SAN FRANCISCO CHAMBER OF COMMERCE

Where smart business starts.

A. Lee Blitch, *President & CEO*
Carol Piasente, *VP of Communications & Events*
Richard Lu, *Art Director*

San Francisco Chamber of Commerce
235 Montgomery Street, 12th Floor
San Francisco, CA 94104
Tel: 415-392-4520
Fax: 415-392-0485
www.sfchamber.com

MARCOA Publishing Inc.

Bart Lally, VP/Publisher
Emily Bates, *Managing Editor*
Andrew Sobel, *Project Manager*
Susan Antonelli, *Account Manager*
Jocelyn Boehm, *VP of Operations*
Rudy Rey, *Client Relations Manager*
Patricia Cross, *Production Manager*
Ray Falvey, *Production Supervisor – Editorial/Cartography*
Ginger Owens, *Production Supervisor – Advertising*
Quinn Cosby, *Production Supervisor – Administration*
Brian J. Davis, *Senior Art Director*
Peter S. Curtis, *Profile Designer*
Jeannie Soverns, *Sales Coordinator*
Julie Her, *Advertising Coordinator*

Cover Design

Brian J. Davis / Ray Falvey

Cover Photos

Codexis
Getty Images
Symyx Technologies Inc.

Profile Writers

Kristen Bole
Andrea Clark
Brendan Doherty

Contributing Writers

Sue Cost
Kathryn Gagnon
Sally Smith Hughes
Frederick K. Koenen
Seema Shah

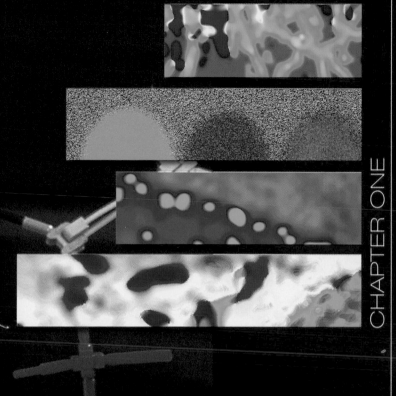

THE HISTORY OF BIOTECHNOLOGY

The Evolution of Genentech

1976 - Dr. Herbert Boyer, who pioneered recombinant DNA technology, started Genentech with Robert Swanson, venture capitalist

1978 - Genentech's scientists clone human insulin

1979 - Human growth hormone cloned by Genentech scientists

1980 - Genentech went public and raised $35 million with an offering that skyrocketed from $35 a share to a high of $88 a share after less than an hour on the market

1982 - First recombinant DNA drug marketed: human insulin (licensed to Eli Lilly)

1984 - First lab production of Factor VIII, a clotting factor for bleeding in hemophiliacs

1985 - Genentech received approval from the FDA to market its first product, Protropin®, growth hormone for children with a deficiency- the first recombinant pharmaceutical product to be manufactured and marketed by a biotech company

1986 - Genentech's interferon alpha-2a (licensed to Hoffmann-LaRoche as Roferon® - A) received FDA approval for the treatment of hairy cell leukemia

1987 - Genentech received FDA approval for Activase® a tissue-plasminogen activator to dissolve blood clots in patients with acute myocardial infarction (heart attack)

1990 - Genentech received FDA approval for Actimmune® for the treatment of chronic granulomatous disease and Genentech's Hepatitis B vaccine (licensed to SmithKline beecham Biologcals S.A.) received FDA approval

1992 - Genentech opened the Founders Research Center, the largest biotechnology research facility in the world

(continued on next page)

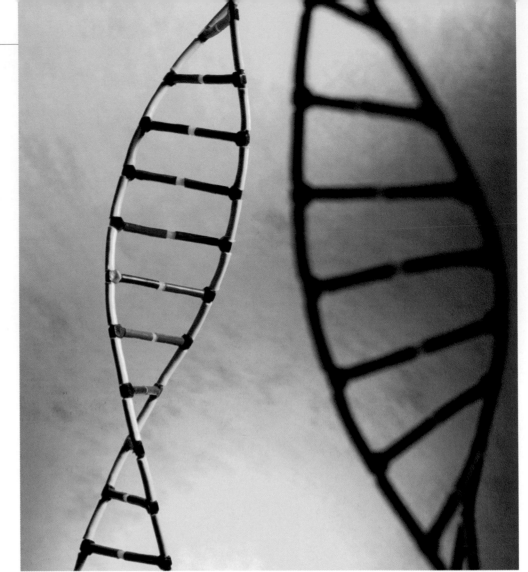

The double helix is a structure that depicts DNA.

A Brief History of Biotechnology in Northern California

by Bay Area Bioscience Center (BayBio)

A university researcher and a venture capitalist formed the world's first biotechnology company, locating it in 3,000 square feet of industrial space in South San Francisco. Genentech, founded in 1976 by University of California, San Francisco (UCSF) biochemist Herbert Boyer and venture capitalist Robert Swanson, was the first of many successful Bay Area biotechnology companies to come.

Genentech followed the direct entrepreneurial lead of pioneering Northern California companies like Cetus Corp., a biological engineering company — the first ever — founded in Berkeley in 1971, and Palo Alto-based Syntex Corp., founded in 1964. Syntex, led by Alejandro Zaffaroni (later a founder of a number of biotech companies), was the first pharmaceutical company to form since World War II.

Much of the work in biotechnology's early years was done by a handful of brilliant investigators and scientists at world-class research institutes — Stanford University, UCSF and University of California, Berkeley (UC Berkeley). Charged by the federal government in the early 1970s to fight a war on cancer, researchers guided by their interest in pushing the frontiers of genetic engineering built more than science — they founded an industry that thrives throughout the Bay Area and is the No. 2 bioscience cluster in the world.

The foundations

Research institutions created the technology, tools and intellectual climate necessary to build a new industry. The Bay Area in the 1960s was percolating innovation and discovery in many quarters, including science. Since the mid-1950s, Stanford, UCSF and UC Berkeley have produced Nobel Laureates in chemistry, physics and biology. In the early 1970s, that tradition of rigorous scientific innovation continued as UC Berkeley biochemist Bruce Ames devised a method, now a standard for researchers, to detect genetic mutations in bacteria. Stanford University's Leonard Herzenberg developed rapid cell-sorters, speeding up research.

In 1973, Boyer, Stanford geneticist Stanley Cohen and Stanford biochemist Paul Berg isolated many of the genetic-engineering methods used in biotech research. Berg linked two genes from different viruses together, and Cohen and Boyer demonstrated that cloning DNA was possible. Cohen and Boyer then proved that they could splice genes into bacteria, using microbes to churn out human hormones, growth factors and other medically important proteins. In just a few short months, these complementary discoveries became the intellectual basis of biotechnology.

Along with the new genetic tools came new fears. Researchers sought to understand the dangers and possibilities that genetic engineering offered. Unsure of the dangers and the regulatory climate they might face, in 1974 Berg and others called for a worldwide discussion on issues of gene splicing and safety. In 1975, at the Asilomar Conference Center in Pacific Grove, 140 prominent researchers and academicians debated their opinions about gene-splicing. Within a year, the National Institutes of Health (NIH) would issue guidelines based upon the conference's recommendations. Swanson and Boyer then founded Genentech, which would win the race to produce the first human proteins using biotech techniques, including insulin (FDA approved in 1982) and the human growth hormone (FDA approved in 1985). Other discoveries were leading to new companies: UCSF's William J. Rutter and two university researchers co-founded Chiron Corp. to find vaccines for hepatitis B. In 1979, the Gladstone Institute of Cardiovascular Disease began research at UCSF.

As science pushed forward, questions regarding patentable science would dominate the headlines. In 1980, the Supreme Court agreed that life forms could be patented. Patents in hand, biotech companies were ready to face Wall Street. Genentech became the first of many companies to go public, generating $35 million in its initial public offering (IPO). A rash of additional public offerings followed as companies attempted to duplicate Genentech's success. Cetus followed in 1981 with a $107 million IPO; Scios, Amgen, Chiron, Xoma and others would follow in the next five years.

Into the 1980s

During its first decade, biotechnology in Northern California experienced tremendous growth. From 1964 through 1977, 84 companies were founded. By 1987, the Bay Area's biotechnology industry had grown to 112 companies, supporting 19,400 jobs and totaling sales of $2 billion. Growth continued throughout the remainder of the 1980s, and between 1987 and 1990, 81 new companies formed. In 1989, Stanford opened the $60 million Beckman Center for Molecular and Genetic Medicine, headed by Nobel Laureate Paul Berg.

An early focus of genetic engineering was agriculture. Again, Northern California was and is at the forefront of the agriculture-biotech (Ag-biotech) revolution.

In 1986, the University of California, Davis founded its program for biotechnology in agriculture. Early in biotech's history, researchers focused their efforts on helping food crops resist frost and pests. Bay Area researchers responded as UC Berkeley professor Steven Lindow and Oakland's Advanced Genetic Sciences created and developed ice-inhibiting bacteria, the first release of a bio-engineered organism in 1987. Calgene Inc. (acquired in 1997 by Monsanto, a food biotechnology company) worked on testing a genetically engineered tomato, later approved in 1994. Groundbreaking agricultural engineering work, begun in Northern California, continues in earnest.

Beyond business success, university researchers and biotechnology institutions are working to cure diseases. Early on, research that led to biotechnology had an anti-cancer goal, but came to include therapies for nearly every disease. A relatively new disease, AIDS, was no different. Researchers began to try and understand the disease immediately. Northern California research led the way as UCSF researchers isolated the HIV virus in 1983.

(continued on page 16)

(continued from last page)

1993 - Genentech received FDA approval for Nutropin®, for treating growth failure in children with chronic renal insufficiency before undergoing kidney transplantation, and Genentech received FDA approval to market Pulmozyme® for treating cystic fibrosis

1996 - Genentech received FDA approval to market Nutropin AQ®, the first and only liquid recombinant human growth hormone for treating growth failure in children with chronic renal insufficiency

1997 - Genentech and partner, IDEC Pharmaceuticals received FDA approval to market Rituxan® for the treatment of patients with relapsed or refractory low-grade or follicular, CD20 positive, B-cell non-Hodgkins lymphoma

1998 - Genentech received FDA approval for Herceptin® as a first-line therapy in combination with paclitaxel and as a single agent in second- and third-line therapy for patients with metastatic breast cancer who have tumors that overexpress the HER2 protein; Genentech also dedicated its new $250 million manufacturing facility in Vacaville—the world's largest for the production of pharmaceutical proteins

1999 - Genentech entered into an agreement with Immunex to grant rights under Genentech's immunoadhesin patent portfolio to Immunex for its product ENBREL®

2000 - Genentech received FDA approval of TNKase™ for the treatment of acute myocardial infarction-it's the first "clot-buster" that can be administered more than five seconds in a single dose and the first package was shipped less than 10 days after agency approval

2001 - The US Patent office granted Genentech and the City of Hope a patent relating to fundamental methods and compositions used to produce antibodies by recombinant DNA technology after 10 years of proceedings

2002 - FDA gives approval for the inclusion of HER2gene detection test in Herceptin product labeling, emphasizing the Dx/Rx link

2003 - Genentech received FDA approval for (Omalizumab), the first biologic for the treatment of asthma. The company has two other compounds under FDA review: Avastin® for colorectal cancer and Raptiva® for psoriasis.

Fathers of the Biotechnology Industry

Herbert Boyer
Genentech Inc.

"*Wonder is what sets us apart from other life forms. No other species wonders about the meaning of existence or the complexity of the universe or themselves.*"

Herbert Boyer's fascination with the universe has led to stellar insights into its wondrous complexity. During the past 30 years, Boyer has been the major force behind the development of recombinant DNA technology. Buttressed by a PhD in bacteriology, Boyer has engendered monumental transformations in human life through academic research, innovative entrepreneurship and humanitarianism.

In 1966, Boyer moved from Pennsylvania to the Bay Area to continue his research in the field of bacterial genetics. While delving into the possibility of DNA modification, he also undertook what would be a lengthy and exceptional teaching career as a biochemistry and biophysics professor at the University of California, San Francisco (UCSF). His research on restrictive enzymes, the bacterial protein that cuts DNA, led to a collaborative discovery that mirrors in greatness that of Watson and Crick's double helix.

Boyer met Stanford professor and geneticist Stanley Cohen, PhD, at a 1973 conference in Hawaii. Upon learning

UCSF Public Affairs

Herbert Boyer, PhD has served as a director of Genentech Inc. since he co-founded the company in 1976 with Robert A. Swanson, a venture capitalist. He also was a vice president of the company from 1976 to 1990.

of the newly obtained data on restrictive enzymes from Boyer's lab at UCSF, Cohen immediately understood that these results could impact his own work in plasmid transformation. Further discussion between the geneticists ensued, and the two Bay Area residents soon recognized that their complementary research could harness the replication power of bacteria, thus manufacturing genes and gene products rapidly and in quantity.

Their collaboration paved the way for the mass production of hormones and other chemicals previously generated solely by the human body. Cohen describes these months in 1973 as a time of unimaginable excitement: "The strategy worked even better than we could have expected and on most days there were new results and a new high. Plasmids were isolated at Stanford, transported to UCSF where they were cut and analyzed, and then transferred back to Stanford where the DNA fragments were joined and the plasmids were reintroduced into bacteria."

Fathering the birth of genetic engineering in research labs so many years ago, Boyer and Cohen may not have realized that the practical uses of their petri dishes would turn to gold, as a new, multimillion-dollar biotech industry emerged. The commercial value of DNA cloning was realized in 1976, when venture capitalist and fellow Bay Area resident Robert Swanson approached Boyer with the idea of marketing the technology to create a drug company. Boyer proved to be more ambitious than some of his colleagues, who believed the commercial application of genetic manipulation was still off in the distant future. Together, the two co-founded Genentech Inc.

José Mercado / Stanford News Service

Stanley Cohen, MD, helped invent a method of cloning genetically-engineered molecules in foreign cells. Cohen's collaboration with Herbert Boyer in 1973 led to three patents and gave birth to an international industry — biotechnology.

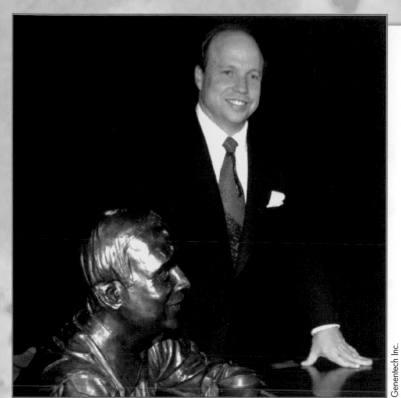

Robert A. Swanson met with Herbert Boyer in 1975, which eventually resulted in the formation of Genentech. Swanson served as director and CEO of Genentech from the time of its inception until 1990, when he was named chair of the board, a position he held until 1996.

Massachusetts Institute of Technology (MIT), understood the challenges inherent in creating a unique and profitable business model for the young science of genetic engineering. He convinced Boyer to entrust his patented creation to a venture with infinite growth potential.

As CEO of Genentech from the time of its inception until 1990, Swanson orchestrated the company's rapid ascension in the new frontier, growing from a '70s start-up to an unmatched leader in the 21ST century's biotechnology industry. By recruiting young talent and fostering a distinctive culture, Genentech's approach to "the business of science" presages the Internet's golden days.

After retiring from Genentech in 1996, Swanson formed K&E Management, a private investment-management firm. He acted as chair of the board of the biotechnology firm Tularik Inc. and was also an active trustee of the San Francisco Ballet, the Museum of Modern Art and the San Jose Tech Center. On December 6, 1999, Robert Swanson died from brain cancer, and the Bay Area biotechnology industry lost a great founding father.

Alejandro Zaffaroni
ALZA Corp.

Alejandro Zaffaroni, a leading San Francisco Bay Area scientist and entrepreneur, was born in Montevideo, Uruguay, in 1923. He was the first Uruguayan émigré to earn a doctorate in biochemistry in the United States. He received his PhD in biochemistry from the University of Rochester and began his research career studying steroids. In 1951, Zaffaroni joined the Mexico City-based chemical firm Syntex. Supervising both research and marketing, Zaffaroni helped transform the small firm into a large pharmaceutical house with research facilities in Palo Alto. The pioneering company's main product at the time — synthetic steroid hormones for contraceptive and dermatological uses — continued to interest Zaffaroni. While examining the negative side effects, his research focused on tempering the standard delivery methods of the steroids. Instead of ingesting a pill or administering a shot, both of which cause a relatively ungovernable rapid release in the

(the name, Boyer's invention, is a contraction of Genetic Engineering Technology), one of the leading biotechnology companies, located in South San Francisco.

In today's world, Genentech's 11 protein-based drugs greatly enhance the quality of life for millions of people suffering from diseases and genetic conditions: metastatic breast cancer and non-Hodgkin's lymphoma patients are receiving treatments that offer a survival benefit, heart-attack victims are receiving injections of a clot-dissolving agent and children with growth difficulties are being treated with human-growth hormone.

The early explosion of the biotechnology industry, begun by Swanson and Boyer, continues to see unabated growth even in today's uncertain economic conditions. Recent press releases cite a $13 billion increase in Genentech's market value due wholly to a high-profile experimental drug, Avastin. Avastin is designed to treat patients in advanced stages of colorectal cancer by cutting off a tumor's blood supply, and may open doors to new treatment therapies for other cancer patients. Genentech exemplifies the enterprise of business acumen and groundbreaking research in biotechnology, continuously fostering the development of beneficial new products.

Robert Swanson
Genentech Inc.

In co-founding Genentech, venture capitalist Robert Swanson proffered the olive leaf of industry to the uninterested university researcher. Swanson's vision of uniting business and biology was the singular opus for the formation of the biotechnology industry, but it required the hand of biochemist Herbert Boyer. Swanson's enthusiasm and remarkable knowledge won Boyer over, as the two discussed the commercial prospects of recombinant DNA in a Bay Area pub. Swanson, with degrees in chemistry and business management from the

In 1968, Alejandro Zaffaroni, PhD, founded the drug-delivery company ALZA Corp., located in Mountain View. Zaffaroni retired from ALZA in 1997 to devote time to the non-profit Zaffaroni Foundation, which he founded in 1963 to research the role of education, nutrition and genetics in the development of depression and addictive disorders.

William J. Rutter, PhD, founded Chiron in 1981, located in Emeryville, and currently serves as chair emeritus. Rutter received the 2003 Biotechnology Heritage Award.

ALZA Corp., DNAX Research Institute (acquired by Schering-Plough), Dynapol (acquired by Dekalb), Affymax N.V. (acquired by Glaxo Wellcome), Affymetrix (partnering with Roche) and Symyx (with 25 corporate partners, including such leading companies as Agfa, Dow Chemical, Exxon-Mobil, Merck and Unilever) are all Zaffaroni start-ups in which the research and development of advanced capabilities have been the key to success.

William J. Rutter
Chiron Corp.

William J. Rutter is a founder of Chiron Corp., a biotechnology company based in Emeryville. He is also professor of biochemistry emeritus at UCSF. Rutter received his BA from Harvard University and his PhD from the University of Illinois. From 1969 to 1982, Rutter was chair of the Department of Biochemistry and Biophysics at UCSF during the period in which the university laboratories, following the discoveries of Herbert Boyer and Stanley Cohen at Stanford, played a key role in the development of recombinant DNA technology and genetic engineering. Rutter served as director of the Hormone Research Institute at UCSF from 1983 to 1989. In 1981, Rutter founded Chiron with two other University of California professors — Edward Penhoet and Pablo Valenzuela. Rutter was chair of Chiron from its inception until 1999, when he became chair emeritas.

Chiron, like Genentech, was a commercial endeavor prompted by the research conducted in UCSF laboratories. The formation of the company was another mark of biologists moving from academia into the business world.

Rutter, Penhoet and Valenzuela founded Chiron in part to develop the hepatitis B vaccine through a contractual relationship with Merck that was initiated at UCSF. Competition, including from former colleagues now working across the bay at Genentech, pushed the founders of Chiron to be innovative in science and business practices. The resulting creation of a recombinant yeast-derived HBsAg was an improved version of the hepatitis B vaccine and was the first of its kind for use in humans. After nine years of research, the US Food and Drug Administration licensed the vaccine for general use in 1986.

In the fall of 1984, Chiron announced that the entire HIV genome was successfully cloned and sequenced for the first time. Another milestone in Chiron's history occurred in 1990, when the FDA licensed the company's hepatitis C antibody blood-screening test. The diagnostic has largely eliminated transmisson of new hepitits C infections through blood transfusion.

Chiron ranks at the top of the biotechnology industry, with $1.3 billion annual revenue in 2002. Originally a 20-person composite of scientists from the founders' UCSF and UC Berkeley laboratories, the company has since grown to more than 5,000 employees. In 1991, Chiron bought Cetus, its neighbor and sometime competitor.

Today, Rutter continues to provide consultation services for biotechnology start-up companies as chair & CEO of Synergenics LLC. Rutter also serves on the board of trustees of the Carnegie Institution of Washington and is a member of the National Academy of Sciences and the American Academy of Arts and Sciences. He has published more than 380 scientific articles and holds more than 20 patents and patent applications.

body, Zaffaroni looked for simple solutions like time-lapse pills and skin patches.

Though he eventually became president of the firm, Zaffaroni resigned from Syntex in 1968, when the company proved reluctant to adapt his drug-delivery concept. This hesitation violated his belief that, "One of the key things to success is never to worry about failing." In an interview conducted by The Tech Museum of Innovation and the *San Jose Mercury News*, Zaffaroni goes on to say: "Many people do not do a lot of the things that could be done because they do not want to have a negative result. If you don't go for the new breakthrough, if you are going just to stay in the areas which we all know, we are stationary...the only thing attractive in life is continually to move forward, to be looking for new opportunities, and to support people and let them fail safely... persistence and how you learn from failure gives you the new path."

During the ensuing years, Zaffaroni's drug-delivery technology has been incorporated in 30 commercialized products marketed worldwide. Located in Mountain View, ALZA is a publicly traded company and the acknowledged leader in drug-delivery systems, with annual revenues reported at $1 billion. In 1981, ALZA marketed Transderm-Scop, the first product incorporating transdermal, or skin patch, technology. The patch is for the prevention of nausea and vomiting associated with motion sickness. A decade later, the company released the first nicotine patch, NicoDerm CQ, which is the No. 1 smoking-cessation product available today. Currently a subsidiary of health-care giant Johnson & Johnson, ALZA's biotechnology and genetic research promotes continual technological evolution.

Zaffaroni has repeatedly recognized the commercial value of risky, leading-edge innovations. He has founded several companies based on business plans that utilize academic laboratories as incubators for ideas that may need larger environments, such as pharmaceutical giants, for technological application.

Ronald Cape
Cetus Corp.

Ronald Cape, a principal pioneer in the biotechnology industry, co-founded Cetus Corp. in 1971. Cape was chair of the board of directors for 20 years and CEO for 13 years until Chiron acquired Cetus in 1991, paying $660 million for the company. Cape, who has a BA in chemistry from Princeton University and an MBA from Harvard University, studied biochemistry. After receiving a PhD from McGill University, he did postdoctoral work in genetics at the University of California, Berkeley (UC Berkeley).

Cetus, headquartered in Emeryville, was taken public in 1981 to complete what was at the time the largest IPO in US history. In 1983, Kary Mullis of Cetus invented the polymerase chain reaction (PCR), which has been hailed as the most revolutionary new technique in molecular biology. Mullis received a PhD in biochemistry from UC Berkeley and joined Cetus Corp. in 1978. PCR, sometimes referred to as "molecular photocopying," amplifies a single DNA molecule into many billions of molecules in several hours. In one application of the technology, small samples of DNA, such as those found in a strand of hair at a crime scene, can produce sufficient copies to carry out forensic tests. PCR quickly became an extremely important technique with direct applications in genetic research, medicine and forensics. For the invention of PCR, Mullis won the Nobel Prize in chemistry in 1993. In 1991, Cetus, which owned the intellectual property rights for the technique (granted in 1989), sold the patent for PCR to Hoffmann-La Roche for $300 million, and, six years later, a new technique combined PCR, DNA chips and a computer program to provide promising advancements in the ongoing search for disease-causing genes.

Under Cape's leadership, Cetus developed therapeutic products to combat cancer and infectious diseases. Interleukin-2 (IL-2) is a human protein in the human body that plays an important role in stimulating the immune system to produce carcinoma-destroying T cells. Proleukin IL-2, a genetically engineered or recombinant version of IL-2, received FDA approval for treatment in kidney cancer in 1992 and for treatment in a type of skin cancer in 1998. In partnerships with other corporations, Cetus explored bioengineering opportunities in food, agriculture, animal health care, instrumentation and diagnostics.

Cape was also a co-founder of Darwin Molecular Corp., which merged with Chiroscience Group PLC in 1996. He is one of seven founding members of the Industrial Biotechnology Association — now the Biotechnology Industry Organization (BIO) — and served as its president for three years. Cape serves on the board of directors of several public and private biotechnology companies, including Caprion, Neugenesis and Ellipsis, of which he is chair. Additionally, he has served on the boards of Princeton University, Rockefeller University and the Whitehead Institute at MIT. Cape is a fellow of several prestigious societies, including the American Academy of Arts and Sciences.

Editorial contributed by Kathryn Gagnon, a freelance writer and editor living in the Bay Area.

Ronald Cape, PhD, is the co-founder and former CEO of Cetus Corp., which was established in 1971 and merged with Chiron in 1991. Cape is a founding member of BIO, a nation-wide organization devoted to life-sciences advocacy.

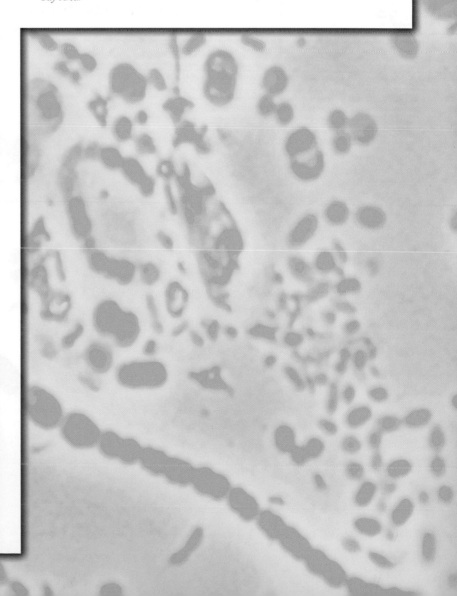

Christine Jegan

Chancellor J. Michael Bishop talks about the plans for the UCSF Mission Bay campus at the Catellus Visitors Center when UC Regents and UC officials toured the area on Sept. 17, 2002.

Stanford

Beckman Center for Molecular and Genetic Medicine

(continued from page 11)

Chiron cloned, sequenced and identified the important coding domains of the virus in 1984, and in 1986, blood screening and diagnostic tests were made available worldwide.

Northern California continued to build on its rich legacy of world-leading research, as UCSF would herald one Nobel Prize that was shared by J. Michael Bishop, who became the 8th chancellor of UCSF in 1997, and Harold E. Varmus for their discovery of the cellular origin of retroviral oncogenes. UCSF garnered another Nobel Prize with Stanley B. Prusiner's award in 1997.

The regulatory climate in the 1980s was evolving as well. The federal government and industry worked to coordinate oversight of genetic engineering. In the early 1990s, an effort by the Clinton administration to reform the nation's health-care system also impacted biotech's prospects by threatening to intervene in pharmaceutical pricing, thus reducing the chances of recouping development costs. Because the biotech industry is evolving, government oversight and regulatory frameworks have shifted frequently.

From the 1990s to tomorrow

Silicon Valley fueled innovation to accelerate the pace of discovery. An entire industry of toolmakers and testing-equipment manufacturers developed as the need for new instruments pushed technology forward, led by research done at Stanford University.

Cetus Corp. (now merged with Chiron Corp.) developed PCR, a chain reaction allowing researchers to generate billions of gene sequence copies in only hours, netting Kary Mullis the Nobel Prize in 1993. Later, tool companies would take techniques learned in the development of silicon chips for high tech and apply them to biotech. The new tools would be necessary for the next big revolution and the next decade of discovery.

The much-publicized Human Genome Project that began in 1990 led to a new basis of drug research and development, from viral replication of proteins to gene-based discovery and treatment of diseases. Again, Northern California research was at the forefront, as Lawrence Livermore National Laboratory and Ernest Orlando Lawrence Berkeley National Laboratory headed up the Western Facility in Walnut Creek, playing a key role in the genome project. In 2000, a working draft of the entire human genome sequence was announced.

With the maturation of a number of early biotech companies, many invested heavily in production facilities. Chiron, Bio-Rad Laboratories, Genentech, Genencor and Bayer built or expanded research and production facilities in the Bay Area. And, just more than 20 years after Genentech's founding, the company began marketing the first genetically engineered monoclonal antibodies aimed at fighting cancer, Rituxan.

Bay Area research universities are currently gearing up for the next wave of research. UCSF is expanding into its Mission Bay campus and is building the California Institute for Quantitative Biomedical Research (QB3), a joint research program between UC Berkeley,

UCSF and University of California, Santa Cruz. Stanford University recently completed the James H. Clark Center for Biomedical Engineering and Sciences, a multi-disciplinary facility to assist in the discovery and understanding of science and medicine. UC Berkeley is undergoing a similar transformation having launched its Health Sciences Initiative, the university is building the Stanley Biosciences and Bioengineering Facility, scheduled to open in 2006. The new Stanley facility will house many of QB3's Berkeley researchers, as well as labs for the College of Engineering's bioengineering department. UC Discovery Grants in Biotechnology was developed in 1996 to help California maintain its leadership position in the biotechnology industry. The grant's research projects in biotechnology are aimed at helping California keep its existing biotech companies, attract more companies and create additional new, high paying jobs.

Linda A. Cicero/Stanford News Service

The James H. Clark Center for Biomedical Engineering and Sciences at Stanford University.

Emerging from a small group of researchers, in less than 30 years biotechnology in the Bay Area has grown to more than 800 companies, employing 85,000 people, generating $4.7 billion in revenue and more than $2 billion in exports annually. But the business, legal, medical and scientific frontiers biotechnology set out to transform and understand have only just begun.

The DNA Puzzle: A Scientific Journey

The most important intellectual discovery in 20th-century biology celebrated its 50th anniversary in 2003. In April 1953, James Watson, Francis Crick and Maurice Wilkins identified the substance of life — the double helical structure of DNA, or Deoxyribose Nucleic Acid. The consequences of the discovery have been developing progressively since 1953 and continue to strongly impact the world today.

At the semi-centennial anniversary of the initial discovery of the structure of DNA, the sequence of genetic information for humans, mice, plants, fruit flies and a host of other organisms has been determined. Watson and Crick may be the renowned fathers of the revolution in genetics, but there are essential players in this pursuit of greater understanding that deserve an equal share of the spotlight. The nature of the competitive struggle for scientific immortality is just as complex as the solved molecule itself.

The science of genetics began in the 19th century with the plant breeding experiments of the Augustinian monk Gregor Mendel. He first presented his findings in 1865, but, unlike Watson and Crick, received little public attention during his lifetime. Rosalind Franklin, another famously marginalized contributor during her lifetime, was a pioneer molecular biologist who worked on the structure at King's College, Cambridge. Professor Maurice Wilkins, Franklin's colleague during her fellowship, had obtained data on the use of X-rays to analyze the DNA structure, and it was his work upon which Franklin advanced images of the structure to a new level of accuracy and decipherability. Dubbed as the "dark lady of DNA" (a phrase apparently coined by Wilkins), Franklin resourcefully created a method for taking high-resolution photographs of single fibers of DNA. X-ray crystallography, an experimental technique that exploits the fact that X-rays are diffracted by crystals, determines the three-dimensional structure of compounds. Franklin's laborious crystallographic work, in particular Photograph 51 (which required 100 hours of exposure), provided the experimental support for the DNA model.

At this time, Watson and Crick were data-poor scientists, unfamiliar with diffraction photo research and inexperienced in the field of chemistry. It is plausible that Franklin would have worked the structure out in due course. Many believe that she didn't quite understand that there was a competition going on. Franklin overlooked the significance of her findings, by which time Watson and Crick had solved the problem, largely through collaboration with scientists in their community.

As Watson writes in his memoir, the Photo 51 image from the King's College laboratory struck in him a sense of "Eureka!," resulting in a leap of faith in the design theory of DNA. Yet it wasn't Franklin who shared the photo with Watson; purportedly she had no knowledge of her competitor having viewed the work. This look at her photo may have been the moment, and the clue, that inspired Watson to piece together the DNA structure as quickly as he did. "The instant I saw the picture my mouth fell open and my pulse began to race," Watson writes in *The Double Helix*. Even after their model was constructed and shown publicly, Franklin was still unaware that it was her work that propelled Watson and Crick to their interpretation of a helical structure.

In 1953, the April 25 issue of the scientific journal *Nature* first presents Watson and Crick's discovery, thus marking a

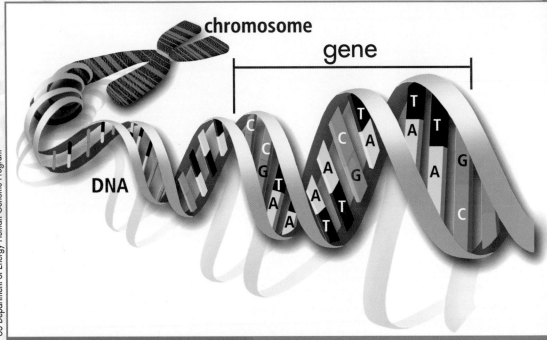

US Department of Energy Human Genome Program

Cells are the fundamental working units of every living system. All the instructions needed to direct their activities are contained within the chemical DNA (deoxyribonucleic acid).

pivotal moment in modern scientific history. The two men were the first of their peer group to successfully compile all the data, theory and sweat; interestingly, they were also of a few to start model making. The momentous *Nature* issue contains Maurice Wilkins' paper as well as a paper by Rosalind Franklin and Raymond Gosling. The publication paved the road to a significantly changed scientific history. Perhaps most importantly, it presented for the first time the crucial diffraction photo — the same photo that first gave Watson the clue to the double helical structure. The X-ray data, published alongside the Watson and Crick paper, matched their structure model exactly, yet was still greatly slighted.

Though scientific research depends on intense collaboration and teamwork, it is also highly competitive. The pressure to solve the double-helix mystery was shared in laboratories around the globe, as scientists attended colloquiums on DNA, reviewed papers, requested meetings and dropped in on each

California Institute of Technology

In 1946, Linus Pauling postulated that the gene might consist of two mutually complementary strands — a concept anticipating Watson and Crick's discovery of DNA structure seven years later. He is the only person ever to receive two unshared Nobel Prizes — for Chemistry in 1954 and for Peace in 1962.

Cold Spring Harbor Laboratory Archives

James Watson and Francis Crick discovered the double helical structure of DNA in 1953.

other. At the California Institute of Technology, far from the Cavendish Laboratory at the University of Cambridge, master chemist Linus Pauling was seeking the molecular holy grail of DNA. His work greatly influenced the studies of Wilkins, the man who would share the Nobel Prize with Watson and Crick.

Other participants in the race to discovery were the youngest-ever recipient of the Nobel Prize and the director of the Cavendish, Sir William Lawrence Bragg; an Austrian chemist, Erwin Chargaff, whose research defined the relationship of the DNA base pairs; and Jerry Donohue, a former student of Pauling. Their research examined theories of the DNA structure that were all building blocks of the foundation for Watson's and Crick's model. It was Chargaff's understanding of the pairing that led to the conclusion that there were two strands; each strand was a complementary mirror image of the other; if separated, each could act as a mold for forming a new double helix identical with the original.

The resulting structure, the hereditary composition of all living cellular organisms, became an aesthetically beautiful icon. More than beautiful though, the structure had meaning. The irresistible model of the DNA structure, which so many scientists strived toward, stunned the world; the genetic-replication process implied by the double helix would be recognized as the miracle of life.

Rosalind Franklin, arguably not given due recognition, was passed over by the Nobel committee for her groundbreaking studies on the crystal structure of DNA;

she was diagnosed with ovarian cancer in 1956, and died on April 16, 1958. The Nobel Prize cannot be awarded posthumously and is also limited to a three-way split. The committee would have had to decide between Franklin and Wilkins — a very difficult choice even without considering all the numerous scientists whose passion and dedication also contributed to solving the structure.

Editorial contributed by Kathryn Gagnon, a freelance writer and editor living in the Bay Area.

Cold Spring Harbor Laboratory Archives

Rosalind Franklin created a method — X-ray crystallography — for taking photographs of single fibers of DNA. One of her images, Photograph 51, provided support for the DNA double-helix model.

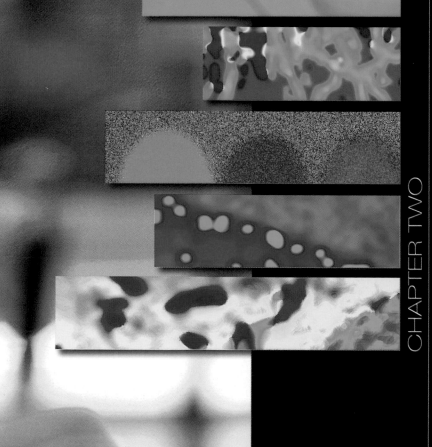

CHAPTER TWO

RESEARCH, INNOVATIONS & EDUCATIONAL INSTITUTIONS

CATELLUS DEVELOPMENT CORP.

University of California, Davis

Art and science converge dramatically in a University of California, Davis sculpture. A suspended ribbon of coiled steel and colored glass, 50 feet tall and 18 inches wide, depicts a snippet of human genetic code.

An Industry Based on the Bay Area's Remarkable Universities

by Frederick Dorey

How do they do it?

For more than 20 years, unique groups of visitors from around the world have made their way to the San Francisco Bay Area, not to visit the established tourist sites, but to traipse around the companies, universities and firms involved in the region's biotechnology industry. They come from various backgrounds and many different regions to study "how we have done it," and plan how they might recreate the Bay Area's success. Many are already familiar with the story of how the Bay Area became the birthplace of the biotechnology industry, but wonder how the Bay Area manages to maintain its position as the preeminent location for this extraordinary business.

While there are many factors in the Bay Area's biotech success, one central fact dominates: The Bay Area is blessed with three pre-eminent research universities that are world leaders in the life sciences — the University of California campuses at San Francisco and Berkeley (UCSF and UC Berkeley) and Stanford University. The three institutions are recognized globally for high-quality scientific research and as the source of many of the fundamental discoveries in modern biology. Since the mid-20th century, these universities, with growing contributions from the University of California campuses at Davis and Santa Cruz (UC Davis and UC Santa Cruz), have attracted talented researchers and remarkably large sums of research funding. As a result, they have produced more innovations — measured by inventions and patent applications in the life sciences — than any other regional group of universities in the world. They have also led the academic world in developing sophisticated technology-transfer organizations, demonstrating how academic inventions may be commercialized to benefit universities, businesses and future patients. The researchers and technology drawn to the Bay Area by these universities have started hundreds of companies in Northern California, from the industry giants like Genentech, Amgen and Chiron, to brand-new start-ups that are launched each year in this region.

In addition, the Bay Area is home to a large, diverse and well-trained scientific workforce that provides staff for companies and research laboratories throughout the Bay Area. This pool of talented local employees is another by-product of the region's research universities and the large and well-established California State University campuses at San Jose, San Francisco, Hayward, Sacramento and Sonoma.

A brief history

The rise to prominence of Bay Area universities in the life sciences can be traced to several factors. Federal government funding of basic biological research increased dramatically in the 1950s, 60s and 70s. Bay Area universities were successful in attracting

Aerial view of Stanford Research Park, 1953. Stanford University's Hoover Tower is visible in upper right area; Varian Associates, the first building in the research park, seen in the foreground.

Varian Associates Inc. Archives

a significant portion of that growing research support. Those research dollars, coupled with the fact that the Bay Area is a very desirable place to live, enabled key department chairs like William J. Rutter at UCSF and Paul Berg at Stanford to attract talented young researchers from around the world.

In the early 1980s, federal legislation known as the Bayh-Dole Act allowed research universities to patent the inventions that had been developed using federal funding. Once patented, those inventions may be licensed into the business world by those universities, which are then free to keep the commercial rewards provided by those patent licenses.

This ability to commercialize the fruits of federal research support without involving the federal bureaucracy, or having to share income with the federal government, was a special boon to the Bay Area. Beginning with the earliest days of the Hewlett-Packard Corp. in the late 1930s, a unique business environment — the Silicon Valley — had developed in Northern California. The commercialization of science through new innovative companies thrived here, first in electronic instruments and components, then in computers and software. These new and risky business endeavors had educated investors, managers, lawyers, real-estate companies and a host of other supporting groups about the challenge of translating new scientific ideas into commercial reality. In short, the biotechnology industry arose in Northern California because the remarkable scientific breakthroughs that were occurring in Bay Area universities were surrounded by a business community that could make them a commercial reality.

Stanford University

Stanford University, a sprawling 8,180-acre campus located on the San Francisco Peninsula, did not only benefit from the growth of the Silicon Valley, it created the Silicon Valley. From its founding in 1891, Stanford fostered an open and supportive policy that allowed its faculty and students to engage in activities outside the university. Its engineering and science departments built on that freedom and helped create many Bay Area technology companies that emerged in the post-World War II period.

As early as the 1950s, Stanford research was being recognized throughout the world. Linus Pauling was awarded the 1954 Nobel Prize in chemistry for his work describing the nature of chemical bonds, and Arthur Kornberg received the 1959 Nobel Prize in medicine and physiology for the artificial production of nucleic acids using enzymes. Paul Berg's 1980 Nobel Prize in chemistry for the development of recombinant DNA techniques recognized the contribution of his work to molecular biology. Then, in the early 1970s, Stanley Cohen, working with Herbert Boyer of UCSF, demonstrated that experimentally recombined DNA

Paul Berg of Stanford University delineated the key steps in which DNA produces proteins.

Stanford's Arthur Kornberg used enzymes to artificially produce nucleic acids.

During a 2000 news conference in San Francisco, three University of California chancellors discussed the Institute for Biomedical Research (QB3) to be headquartered at UCSF's Mission Bay. The chancellors are, from left, M.R.C. Greenwood of UC Santa Cruz, Robert M. Berdahl of UC Berkeley and J. Michael Bishop of UCSF. QB3 is a joint program of all three campuses.

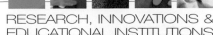

could be put into cells and function successfully. The Cohen-Boyer recombinant DNA discovery was perhaps the pivotal development of modern biotechnology.

But as the history of the Cohen-Boyer invention demonstrates, Stanford was a pioneer in another critical area of the modern biotechnology industry — the art of successfully transferring technology from its academic source to the business world.

In the 1970s, few academic researchers in the life sciences were attuned to the process of protecting inventions with patents, and the value that licensing such patents might have for both the universities and themselves. When the Cohen-Boyer invention was discussed at Stanford and UCSF, there was little expectation that it could be of commercial value. Neils Reimers, who started Stanford's Office of Technology Licensing in 1969, recognized that without patent protection, if a new invention did have commercial value, Stanford and UCSF would gain nothing from it. With one week to spare, Reimers convinced the inventors to support a patent filing. Reimers' office administered the patenting and licensing of the Cohen-Boyer invention. It was a remarkable piece of work. When the patent finally expired in 1996, it had earned more than $220 million that was split between Stanford and UCSF. From that success, Stanford became one of the leaders in structuring and approving the transfer of technology developed (or improved) at the university to private companies.

Stanford's impact on the business environment does not end at the technology-office door. Stanford is also home to the first, and still most successful, university-linked business park in the world. Developed on 700 acres at the southern end of Stanford's property, Stanford Research Park signed its first tenant lease, Varian Associates, in the early 1950s. Growing steadily from that time, the area is now home to roughly 140 companies with about 23,000 employees. These companies cover the full range of technologies including biotechnology, bioinformatics, medical devices and service firms that support the Silicon Valley.

In the early 1970s, Dr. Stanley Cohen (above) of Stanford University partnered with Dr. Herbert Boyer (below) of UCSF to demonstrate that experimentally recombined DNA could be put into cells and function successfully. The Cohen-Boyer recombinant DNA discovery was perhaps the pivotal development of modern biotechnology.

The Parnassus Heights campus at UCSF is home to graduate professionals attending the schools of dentistry, medicine, nursing and pharmacy.

The University of California, San Francisco

The statewide University of California (UC) system has two flagship campuses in the immediate San Francisco Bay Area — Berkeley and San Francisco. While both campuses were originally organized before 1875, the San Francisco campus has, from its beginning, focused exclusively on the health sciences, including basic research in a number of related disciplines such as biochemistry and molecular biology. These two Bay Area campuses, Berkeley and San Francisco, have had the remarkable good fortune to be the pre-eminent public university sites in a spectacular region of a state that saw unparalleled growth and prosperity during the second half of the 20th century. The scientific reputation of these campuses, combined with the Bay Area's remarkable beauty, renowned lifestyle and mild

(continued on page 28)

Nobel Laureates

The year 2000 marked the 100th anniversary of the Nobel Prize. Universities and research institutions throughout California — which claim more Nobel laureates than any region in the world, had ample reason to celebrate the centennial. The Bay Area is home to 47 Nobel Prize recipients. Faculty and researchers affiliated with the University of California (UC) have won 45 Nobel Prizes, including 14 prizes since 1995. Twenty-two of the laureates are affiliated with UC schools in the Bay Area. Stanford University claims 25 prize-winning faculty, three of whom are affiliated with the Hoover Institution.

UCSF Public Affairs

Stanley B. Prusiner, Nobel Prize in physiology or medicine, 1989

Memorial Sloan-Kettering Cancer Center

Harold E. Varmus, Nobel Prize in physiology or medicine, 1989

University of California, San Francisco

J. Michael Bishop, Nobel Prize in physiology or medicine, 1989

UC Berkeley Public Affairs

Yuan T. Lee, Nobel Prize in chemistry, 1986

The Nobel Prize offers awards in the fields of physics, chemistry, physiology or medicine, economics, literature and peace. One prize for each category is awarded annually. The Nobel Foundation, which oversees awards was established in 1900 based on the will of Alfred Nobel. The foundation is not involved in the selection process and the final choice of the laureates. The first Nobel Prizes were awarded in 1901. Awards are closely linked to the history of modern science, the arts and political development.

Linda A. Cicero/Stanford News Service

Paul Berg, Nobel Prize in chemistry, 1980

Bancroft Library's Bioscience and Biotechnology Program

In 1997, the Bancroft Library at the University of California, Berkeley (UC Berkeley) launched the Program in the History of the Biological Sciences and Biotechnology. The program conducts oral histories with individuals in academia and industry, and also collects archives that include personal and corporate papers, correspondence, research reports, photographs and other primary resources that are made available for research. Scholars are interested in biotechnology because of its far-reaching impact on health, agriculture, business and society.

Oral histories have been conducted with prominent bioscientists, including Paul Berg, Herbert Boyer, Stanley Cohen, Arthur Kornberg and William Rutter. Additional oral histories address health and industrial issues closely related to biotechnology, including a series on the AIDS epidemic. Some of the oral histories and related material are available online.

An advisory board, whose members include distinguished scientists, corporate leaders, historians and scholars throughout the Bay Area, provides oversight of the program.

UC Berkeley is recognized as a global center for research into the history of biomolecular science and biotechnology.

Editorial contributed by Sally Smith Hughes, science historian in the Regional Oral History Office, The Bancroft Library.

First meeting of Program in the History of the Biological Sciences and Biotechnology Advisory Board on October 7, 1996. From left to right: Frederick Dorey, Charles Faulhaber, Stanley Cohen, Roger Hahn, William Rutter, Edward Penhoet, Gunther Stent, Sally Hughes, Peter Hanff, Robert Swanson and Daniel Koshland.

(continued from page 25)

climate, have made positions at UC Berkeley and UCSF much sought-after prizes for talented researchers from around the world.

UCSF, highly regarded since its inception, graduated into the top tier of biomedical research centers in the 1960s and 70s as several key researchers created an exciting scientific environment that attracted other talented researchers and remarkable sums of research support. William J. Rutter, who, in 1969, became chair of the Department of Biochemistry (and later co-founder of Chiron), helped create an environment that brought together the likes of J. Michael Bishop and Harold Varmus, who shared the Nobel Prize in physiology or medicine in 1989 for their discovery regarding oncogenes — the finding that normal cellular genes can be converted to cancer genes. Varmus would later be director of the National Institutes of Health (NIH) and president of Memorial Sloan-Kettering Cancer Center in New York. Bishop became chancellor of UCSF in 1999. Herbert Boyer, co-inventor of recombinant DNA, was also a member of the UCSF Department of Biochemistry in the 1970s. Also joining UCSF in this era was Stanley Prusiner, who would be awarded the Nobel Prize in Medicine in 1997 for the discovery of prions, a previously unknown infectious agent responsible for rare infections such as mad cow disease.

UCSF's place in the history of biotechnology will be forever secured by the founding of Genentech Inc. In 1976, Robert Swanson, then a 28-year-old venture capitalist with the firm Kleiner Perkins Caufield & Byers, drove from Silicon Valley to UCSF for a meeting with Boyer. Swanson had the idea that recombinant DNA could be utilized to make pharmaceutical products. Their meeting adjourned to a local pub, and Genentech was born.

During the years, the relationship between Genentech and UCSF would have its share of twists and turns, sometimes contentious, sometimes supportive. By 2003, the first of the major new buildings to be erected in UCSF's new Mission Bay Campus would be named Genentech Hall and funded, in part, through a $50 million contribution from Genentech.

Two years after Genentech's founding, another biotech cornerstone company, Amgen, was incorporated in San Francisco. And, in 1981, Rutter, along with UCSF biochemist Pablo Valenzuela and UC Berkeley biochemist Edward Penhoet, founded Chiron, located in Emeryville, which is currently another leader of the biotech industry.

Today, UCSF has several major sites throughout San Francisco, including its 107-acre main campus on Parnassus, located above Golden Gate Park, and the new second campus at Mission Bay. The university is comprised of four schools, Medicine, Dentistry, Nursing and Pharmacy and is affiliated with the San Francisco Veterans Administration Hospital and San Francisco General Hospital. It is home to 11 different research institutes and has consistently ranked among the top universities in the nation for the amount of research funding awarded by the NIH.

An investment in the future shared by state and private industry, the Institute for Quantitative Biomedical Research (QB3) opened in the fall of 2004 at UCSF's Mission Bay campus. This is one of the California Institutes for Science and Innovation developed at the initiative of Governor Gray Davis. QB3, a collaboration between UCSF, UC Berkeley and UC Santa Cruz, brings the tools of the physical and computational sciences to biomedical research. This will further understanding of biological systems at all levels of complexity - from atoms and proteins to cells, tissues, organs and the entire organism. The long-sought integration will allow scientists to attack problems that have previously been unapproachable and is expected to lead to fundamental new discoveries, new drugs and new technologies for human health.

The University of California, Berkeley

The University of California was founded in 1868, with the first classes held on the new Berkeley campus in 1873. Its growth and advancement in the academic world, from a small, struggling western university to one of the great research universities of the world, mirrors the growth of California. UC Berkeley emerged into the arena of world-class scientific research in the 1930s through the work of E. O. Lawrence, PhD, and the creation of the first cyclotron. Other achievements included isolation of the human polio virus and the discovery of all the artificial elements heavier than uranium. It is no coincidence that two elements of the Periodic Table are named after Berkeley and California. Researchers from UC Berkeley, including Lawrence Berkeley National Laboratory, have been awarded 18 Nobel Prizes.

Watercolor rendering of the planned Stanley Biosciences and Bioengineering Facility. Groundbreaking for the new building was in 2003.

UC Berkeley is pre-eminent in the field of nanotechnology, leads the state-sponsored Center for Information Technology Research in the Interest of Society (CITRIS) and is a key participant in QB3. It is also home to the Wills Neuroscience Institute.

UC Berkeley has also led the way in supporting faculty entrepreneurship and economic development in Northern California. In 1990, it was the first UC campus to establish its own technology-transfer office that was separate from the UC systemwide structure.

That change has helped Berkeley provide key licenses to important technologies, such as DNA sequencers and reagents — fundamental tools that enabled the sequencing of the human genome. UC Berkeley licenses have produced more than $28 million in revenues for the university since 1998, including five of the top 25 revenue-generating inventions in the UC system. Licenses and option agreements from Berkeley have attracted millions of dollars of corporate-sponsored research for the university. Berkeley faculty and students have founded more than 60 start-up companies, including some of the most important names in the Bay Area biotechnology industry, such as Chiron, Tularik and Exelixis.

University of California, Davis

Founded in 1908 as the University of California Farm School, UC Davis is today a large, comprehensive public university. By building on its original foundation, two parts of the university that deal with life sciences — the Davis College of Agricultural and Environmental Sciences and the School of Veterinary Medicine — are recognized world leaders in those fields. With research funding usually ranking among the top 20 universities in America, research at UC Davis has produced numerous scientific achievements in the life sciences and has shaped the products and processes of modern agriculture. Revenue from UC Davis' patent licenses ranks second among all campuses in the UC system. Davis' leadership role in the still-developing worlds of agricultural and environmental biotechnology and the commercial impact of its innovations will continue to grow.

(continued on page 32)

Taking a Creative Approach to Technology Transfer

by Sandra J. Miller

In the past 20 years, the San Francisco Bay Area has emerged as a premier region for medical-device development. Within a 50-mile radius of Stanford University, there are more than 400 medical-device companies that range in size from global corporations with several thousand employees to start-ups with a few inventors working out of a garage. Since 1995, more than $3.75 billion in venture capital has been invested in the Silicon Valley medical-device sector.[1] This activity accounts for an average of 32 percent of all medical-device venture-capital investment in the same period, compared with 12 percent, 9 percent and 8 percent for the New England, San Diego and Los Angeles/Orange County regions, respectively.

Many of the key innovators and founders in the regional medical-device industry have Stanford roots. Well-known examples include doctors Thomas Fogarty, Eberhard Grube, William New, Rodney Perkins, John Simpson, Simon Stertzer and Paul Yock. As a group, Stanford faculty in the Schools of Medicine and Engineering have authored more than 250 medical-device patents and are on the scientific advisory boards or are key consultants to roughly 100 medical-device companies.

It is no great surprise that the "regional advantage" of networking among technology-savvy individuals applies in the medical-technology sector as well. In today's fast-paced medical-device industry, technical breakthroughs, start-ups, mergers and acquisitions occur at a dizzying speed. Entrepreneurs who thrive in this scene have been able to create robust personal networks operating at many levels (venture, legal, entrepreneurs, large and small companies, and so forth).

The Stanford Biodesign Network (BDN) was formed in 1998[II] to help faculty and students at Stanford — who invent and test new medical technologies — make better and faster connections to these real-world R&D networks. BDN is a collection of more than 1,200 university and biomedical-technology industry participants. Through its Web-based networking resource, BDN provides links to the professional communities that specialize in biomedical technology, such as investors (angel, venture capital and institutional), manufacturers and attorneys who practice intellectual property and new venture formation.[III]

As part of this effort, BDN has developed a special partnership with the Stanford Office of Technology Licensing (OTL), a pioneering university tech-transfer organization that is highly regarded worldwide for its ongoing success. The strategy behind the OTL-BDN partnership is to combine the licensing expertise of OTL with the technology domain expertise of BDN. The combination is designed to try to mitigate some of the key challenges faced by academic technology-licensing offices: Most of these offices have a heavy caseload, with severely limited resources compared to a venture business. Second, university technology-licensing offices are responsible for managing a highly diverse technology portfolio, with inventions ranging from new molecules to jet engines. Third, licensing offices rely on the inventors as their most effective source of licensing prospects. According to *The Journal of the Association of University Technology Managers,*

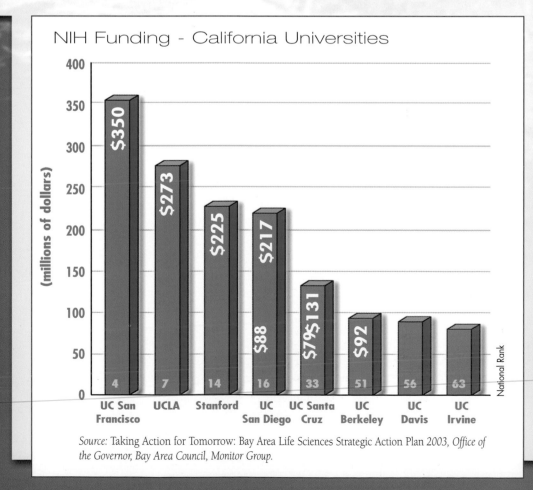

Source: Taking Action for Tomorrow: Bay Area Life Sciences Strategic Action Plan *2003, Office of the Governor, Bay Area Council, Monitor Group.*

Bay Area Technology Commercialization Process

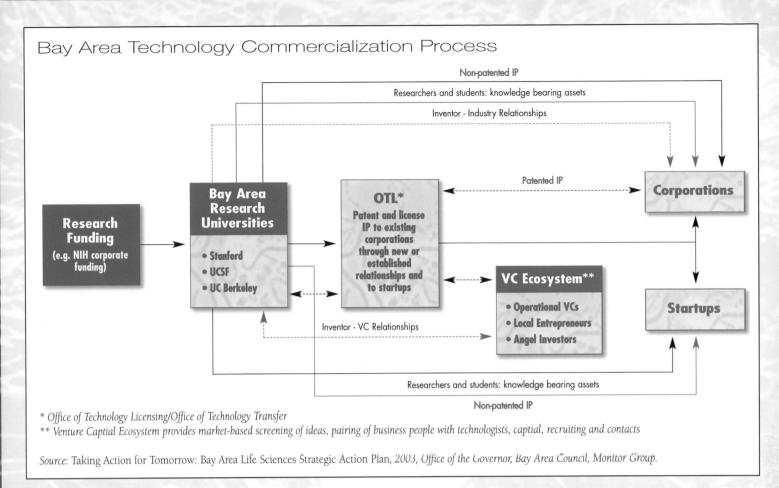

* Office of Technology Licensing/Office of Technology Transfer
** Venture Captial Ecosystem provides market-based screening of ideas, pairing of business people with technologists, captial, recruiting and contacts

Source: Taking Action for Tomorrow: Bay Area Life Sciences Strategic Action Plan, 2003, Office of the Governor, Bay Area Council, Monitor Group.

Harrison F. Dillon's 1999 study examining the sources for licensing leads found that the majority of successful leads (54 percent) originated from the inventor providing information and industry contacts to the licensing professional.[IV] This represents a problem for many inventors — particularly first-timers — who may have only slim or haphazard knowledge of the industry.

BDN addresses the first two issues — resources and domain expertise — by means of a full-time executive director and a faculty leadership group. The executive director works with the OTL associate responsible for a given invention to develop a plan for further testing, development and/or marketing of the innovation. This frequently involves seeking the opinion of one of the faculty leadership group (or appropriate persons in their network).

Although the impact on technology-transfer outcomes is difficult to measure, there are early indications that the BDN-OTL partnership is productive. The number of active med-tech dockets (technology disclosures) has grown significantly since 1999. Perhaps more impressive, seven new med-tech companies have come from Stanford-related founders since 1999, all of which have had substantial roots in the BDN "germination" process.[V]

Whatever the impact on "deal flow", the primary goal of BDN remains an educational one — to help faculty and students come to a better understanding of the technology-transfer process. The most effective way to deliver this education is through individual mentoring, working with the faculty and students on their specific inventions. In addition to this substantial mentoring activity, BDN has developed several educational programs, including graduate and undergraduate courses in medical-device innovation, design and prototyping.

A key assumption behind BDN is that there is a real potential for stimulating new device inventions within the university if conditions are right. These conditions include: 1) a recognition of device innovation at the university as an important part of the academic mission; 2) cross-pollination within departments and between the university and industry; 3) attention to identifying potentially productive areas for invention; and 4) availability of mentoring by experts with real-world experience in device development. Notably, each of the innovators mentioned earlier, as well as many others, are active Biodesign mentors and often lecture in Stanford medical-device courses and seminars.

Northern California University Spin-off Companies

INSTITUTION	BIOMEDICAL COMPANIES*
Caltech	24
Lawrence Berkeley/Lawrence Livermore National Labs	7
Stanford University	94
UC Berkeley	39
UC Davis	18
UC San Francisco	60
UC Santa Cruz	3
TOTAL	221

* Number of biomedical companies founded by faculty or alumni or based on university technology — includes companies with multiple university connections.

Source: CHI Survey, 2001

Biomedical Development Center

Growing biotechnology businesses in the Bay Area

The San Francisco Bay Area is home to some of the most prestigious biomedical-research institutions in the world, which often result in start-up businesses established by faculty and students of these institutions. Start-up bioscience businesses face many challenges, which are increasingly daunting, as venture-capital financing for early-stage bioscience companies has become more difficult to obtain. The Biomedical Development Center (BDC) at Mission Bay was created in response to both the promise of biomedical research at research institutions and the difficulties entrepreneurial scientists wishing to develop their discoveries face.

BDC is a newly established company located near the University of California San Francisco's (UCSF) Mission Bay campus. The Biomedical Development Center was organized, in close cooperation with UCSF, to assist start-up bioscience companies that are seeking to further develop their cutting-edge discoveries and technologies. BDC will assist these institutions in advancing the development of research.

One of BDC's major functions will be establishing businesses. BDC will assist start-up companies, including professional and business support in the preparation of business plans, assistance with grant applications and advice on financing. Laboratory space will be provided.

(continued on next page)

Debbie Aldridge, Public Communications/University Relations, UC Davis

The administration building at University of California, Davis, as seen from across the arboretum waterway.

(continued from page 29)

University of California, Santa Cruz

Although one of the newest campuses of the University of California system, Santa Cruz has made a great impact in several areas of the life sciences. In particular, UC Santa Cruz's contribution to bioinformatics, which is the use of computers to organize and analyze vast amounts of basic biological information, helped make possible the sequencing of the human genome. UC Santa Cruz posted the first site of the assembled human genome sequence on the World Wide Web for the benefit of academic researchers, companies and regulators throughout the world.

UC Santa Cruz is home to the NIH-funded Center for Biomolecular Science and Engineering (CBSE), which is one of 19 centers around the world that make up the International Human Genome Mapping Consortium. CBSE features an interdisciplinary program that focuses on research and academia in the post-genomic arena.

An image of Science Hill at the University of California, Santa Cruz.

Conclusion

Of the gifts that gave rise to the biotechnology industry in Northern California, none has proven more important than its research universities. These institutions have been a source of scientific innovation, research leadership and a well-qualified scientific workforce that has not been equaled elsewhere. Great research flourishing in a business environment that knows how to develop it has produced a model for commercial innovation that is the envy of the world. More than 500 life-sciences companies throughout the world can include in their origins some combination of people, ideas, innovation or products that were originally developed in Bay Area universities. It is a remarkable gift to the world, and it will surely grow in the years ahead.

(continued from last page)

BDC will also provide start-up clients with early-stage capital by establishing a capital fund through which BDC can make direct investments into the client companies. BDC will also assist client companies with obtaining financing from other sources, such as government grants and research partnerships with industry.

A further goal of the BDC will be to assist the academic research institutions whose scientists have begun developing technologies. UCSF averages 150 invention disclosures from its scientists per year. The vast majority of these technologies are insufficiently developed at the early-stages to attract licensing or financing from industry or venture-capital sources on desirable terms to the research institution. BDC will allow scientists to further develop these technologies to the point that they are more readily licensed to industry or can secure investor interest.

The founders of BDC are Foley & Lardner, an international-law firm with a large life-sciences practice; Titan Venture Partners, a San Francisco-based investment and management company; and Joseph Bouckaert, BDC's managing director. BDC is a for-profit entity located in San Francisco.

Editorial contributed by Frederick K. Koenen, partner in the San Francisco office of Foley & Lardner, where he practices corporate and securities law.

Majed

Genentech Hall

UCSF Mission Bay
A new campus for teaching, research and health

UCSF Mission Bay is fast becoming a realized vision. It encompasses a second major UCSF campus dedicated to teaching, research and health — a campus designed to spur collaborations and speed the pace of biomedical discovery. Located south of SBC Park with a commanding view of downtown San Francisco, the new campus will double the university's research and teaching space.

The new UCSF campus has transformed land once occupied by old warehouses and rail yards. Catellus Development Corp. donated 30 acres of the site, and the city of San Francisco donated an additional 13 acres. UCSF Chancellor J. Michael Bishop presided over groundbreaking ceremonies for the new campus in 1999.

Research is now well underway in the first building, UCSF Genentech Hall, which opened in 2003. Two other research buildings are under construction, both of which should be completed in 2004. Two additional buildings are also under construction. The 43-acre campus will be developed in phases during the next 15 to 20 years and at full build-out will have 20 structures and an expected UCSF population of 9,100.

As the pace quickens at Genentech Hall and the other campus buildings to follow, the new UCSF community will likely attract a range of public and private enterprises — not only businesses to serve the growing population of students, faculty and staff in this once-sleepy part of San Francisco — but also life-science companies drawn to UCSF's research expertise.

Research in UCSF Genentech Hall focuses on structural and chemical biology, as well as molecular and developmental biology and related fields. The building is also home to UCSF's Molecular Design Institute and the Center for Advanced Technology. Faculty, post-doctoral scientists, students and staff began moving in during the first week of 2003, and Genentech Hall was fully occupied by spring 2003. The five-story building includes a bookstore, library and a café.

Collaboration is crucial

Genentech Hall, like other Mission Bay campus buildings, was designed to encourage interaction — both formal and informal — between scientists in related disciplines. For example, the fifth floor brings chemists and chemical biologists together, boosting the effort to translate research insights into new drugs and other treatment strategies.

The new building supports the largest concentration of chemists in any medical-pharmacy school building in the country. Chemists can subtly modify the structure of molecules

Mission Bay

Catellus Development Corp.

QB3 headquarters. The institute brings together expertise in the physical sciences, engineering and mathematics to help tackle biological problems of such complexity that they simply cannot be approached with the tools of just one discipline.

Room for art and recreation

Work has also begun on the four-story Campus Community Center, targeted for completion in fall 2004, and on UCSF Mission Bay's housing complex, currently designed to include 431 units with more than 750 beds for students, post-doctorate students and scholars. The plan is to complete construction by 2005.

The new UCSF campus will also include Koret Quad, a 3.2-acre space designed to serve as an informal, landscaped gathering place for the public, as well as faculty, staff and students. The entire campus is expected to have at least eight acres of publicly accessible open space.

Construction funds for the new campus are coming from a variety of state, university and private sources. The expected cost of the UCSF Mission Bay Campus at completion is estimated at about $1.5 billion.

active in cells or create new molecules to determine, for example, the role specific proteins play in signaling between and within cells. This detailed knowledge is vital both to understand living systems at a molecular level and to develop drugs that can counter malfunctions.

Genentech Hall Lounge areas offer open views of the San Francisco skyline, as well as their own shadow show.

Majed

The second campus structure, the Genetics, Development and Behavioral Sciences Building, is targeted for occupancy early in 2004.

In late 2004, researchers and administrators will move into the new Institute for Quantitative Biomedical Research (QB3), the third research building in UCSF Mission Bay's initial phase of development. QB3 is a partnership between UCSF, UC Berkeley and UC Santa Cruz — one of the California Institutes for Science and Innovation developed at the initiative of the governor. The UCSF building will be the

By any measure, UCSF is one of the world's premier health-sciences universities, a leader in biomedical research, patient care, higher education and public service. By the 1980s and 1990s, the university's research enterprise was bursting at its seams, rich in creative potential, but poor in space to fully realize that potential. The new campus at Mission Bay offers UCSF a new life, assuring that its faculty scientists, post-docs and graduate students can gain momentum as they explore the fundamental workings of cells and of molecules that underlie new treatments to improve human health.

CHAPTER THREE

FINANCING BIOTECHNOLOGY

The venture-capital industry invests money into biotechnology companies.

The Birth of the Biotech Industry

by G. Steven Burrill

Tom Perkins was an early investor in Genentech.

Capital — be it venture, public-equity, private or government — continues to be biotech's source of sustenance. But were it not for a handful of San Francisco Bay Area businesspersons with a penchant for understanding what a new realm of science could do for the future, biotech might never have become an industry.

This new industry began in the Bay Area in the early 1970s. Those involved ultimately coined the word "biotechnology" to capture the business of pioneering recombinant DNA, genetic engineering and monoclonal antibody technology. It seemed to be a different era as science and financing began to unfold into new markets and technologies.

The challenge was to apply the science from Stanford University, the University of California, San Francisco (UCSF), the University of California, Berkeley (UC Berkeley), the University of California, Davis and the California Institute of Technology and turn it into monetary value. At that point in time, there was no historical data to guide researchers and venture capitalists (VCs).

As the economist Hernando de Soto writes in *The Mystery of Capital*, "The great practitioners of capitalism ... were able to reveal and extract capital where others saw only junk, by devising new ways to represent the invisible potential that is locked up in the assets we accumulate." That is precisely what those who were pioneering ways to finance biotechnology had to do.

Although Alejandro Zaffaroni founded ALZA Corp. in 1968 (*see sidebar, "Keeping ALZA Afloat", pg. 42*) and Cetus Corp. was established by Ronald Cape in 1971, it was the formation of Genentech Inc. in 1976 that really launched the biotech industry. Robert Swanson, who with Herbert Boyer helped create Genentech, was at the time a partner with the VC firm of Kleiner Perkins Caufield & Byers. Swanson convinced his boss, Tom Perkins, to take a look at the company.

Perkins recalls: "When we put together Genentech, it was an extraordinarily high-risk venture. No other VCs were interested in participating, and so we did all of the initial financing. The primary investment in Genentech was only $100,000, but during the 20 years that I was chair of the board, I helped the company raise more than $3 billion.

"Few investors cared about Genentech in the beginning, and, if anybody did, they just assumed it was some sort of screwball experiment. But once Genentech did what it said it would do, then the company became the most important new thing. Huge amounts of money started to flow into biotechnology, and Genentech made it all possible.

"A huge amount of money went into creating Genentech throughout the years — more money than would be required for anything in electronics. Did I see that very clearly in the beginning? No, not at all. As it turned out, Genentech was profitable from early on."

One vehicle for financing that was a brainchild of Perkins was the idea of R&D partnerships, whereby investors fund the FDA trials. These partnerships paid for the trials and then licensed the products back to Genentech. There were other revenue streams, as well, including research contracts from large pharmaceutical companies (big pharma). Eventually there were the products.

Genentech's initial public offering (IPO) was a huge success, raising $35 million. Shares were offered at $35 a share, and, within one hour, the stock was selling for $88. It ended the day trading at more than $60 a share.

"It was headline stuff," Perkins remembers. "People perceived that Genentech was new, different and extremely important and that we could be hugely successful. Genentech was all about scientific achievement and truly valuable technology, highly patented products, saving lives and so forth."

Financing passion

Of course, the same cannot be said of all biotech investments. Cetus, for example, raised more than $1 billion, but sold its most valuable asset — its PCR technology — for $300 million to Hoffman-La Roche Inc. in 1991. Cetus then bet the ranch on interleukin-2 (IL2), which did not deliver. In 1991, Chiron staged a $660 million takeover of Cetus, which may be viewed as a disappointing final act for a company that was so hot when it IPO'd in 1981 that it made history as the second-largest initial public stock offering in US history, selling 5.2 million shares at $23, raising $122 million.

Frederick Frank, vice chair and director of Lehman Brothers Inc., was at the forefront. He recounts: "The financing in those days was fun. We were financing passion and dreams. We were financing technology ideas and there were all sorts of established agricultural, food and industrial companies that were clamoring to partner with the biotech industry in order to have a window on the emerging technology.

"The success of Genentech and Cetus, as well as a number of other companies, created a new paradigm that I call 'publicly-traded venture-capital companies.' In the mid-1980s, a

Frederick Frank is a venture-capitalist with the biotech industry.

miraculous thing took place — financing shifted to a substantial new cornucopia of capital from R&D partnerships, which took advantage of the tax code that allowed investors to get a tax credit of 50 percent on day one if they invested in one of these fledgling companies. All of the early biotech companies took advantage of these R&D partnerships and raised a great deal of money.

"As we moved into the early 90s, we went through periods in which the concept began to be articulated: The window is either open or closed. That reflected what will continue to be the case — that when a company IPOs and goes to premiums, excitement takes place and more companies try to go public. Clearly, in time, there are more companies seeking capital than there is money, and the window shuts. In the 90s, we also began investing not only in concepts, but also in products that were entering clinical phases of development. Of course, with clinical trials, you get clinical failures, and there were some rather spectacular failures that caused volatility in the publicly traded markets.

"Another phenomenon that took hold at that time were collaborations. Two transactions epitomize what was taking place. One was the $125 million collaboration between SmithKline and Human Genome Sciences. Outscaled compared to anything that had been done, that deal served as validation and brought attraction to the whole area of genomics. The other was the Genentech-Roche deal, again outsized, which was a unique transaction involving the investment of $500 million up front by Roche to purchase 50 percent of Genentech from the shareholders at a 67 percent premium, which put a theoretical value on that company of $7 billion. So now you have another industry approval, creating enormous value.

"Now let's get to 1994, when we filed an offering for Ligand Pharmaceuticals in San Diego. By the time we were at the SEC waiting for regulatory authorizations, the window closes. I came back to Ligand's CEO with a new concept for financing that did take Ligand public — a security called Internal Rate of Return of Common Stock. It provides a downside protection to the new investor, meaning that if the stock can't appreciate at 20 percent a year in each of the first two years, the shareholders will be issued additional shares to bring them up to that point in time.

"The tax code changed around 1994, so the tax advantage of R&D partnerships was basically nullified and that form of financing literally died. As a result, the marketplace was very responsive to having investment bankers create another vehicle for financing these companies."

Riding the waves

Venture capitalists make sure investors understand the risks and the rewards of this ever-evolving, technology-based industry. Initially, it was an unnatural for a big company and a little company to conduct a transaction in which both companies were equal and for which they shared risk. During the course of time, it became more natural, but in the early days with Cetus and ALZA, approaching big pharma was highly unusual.

The early venture capitalists were creating a series of companies for which there were awesome financing requirements. It was necessary to develop vehicles to attract capital to fund long-term technology for product development — and do it in an environment where expectation may get ahead of reality.

Had the barriers been recognized, progress might not have been made. A good entrepreneur does not recognize barriers, but instead focuses on solving problems. At some level, the early VCs were naive about the time and the money that financing biotech was ultimately going to take. So VCs would raise enough money to reach the next level and the next, while incrementally stepping up valuations and, presumably, reducing risk.

Samuel D. Colella spent 20 years managing companies before he became a venture capitalist in 1984. Now with Versant Ventures, Colella funded CV Therapeutics and Tularik Inc. in the Bay Area, as well as numerous biotech companies elsewhere.

"Biotech was exploding in the mid- to late-80s, and I was on 16 or 17 company boards and starting five or six companies a year. The evidence created by earlier companies like Genentech fueled biotechnology," Colella recalls. "Their dreams were beginning to show reality, and we started to see products. This gave us confidence that we were on the right track. We were meeting outstanding scientists and researchers. It was a fertile time and there weren't that many venture capitalists. Today, there are many more people in this business, it is more competitive and it certainly is not as collegial as it was.

Rudi Weislein

Samuel D. Colella was a pioneering venture capitalist for the biotechnology industry.

Venture-Capital Investment in Northern California Biomedical Industry, 1995-2000

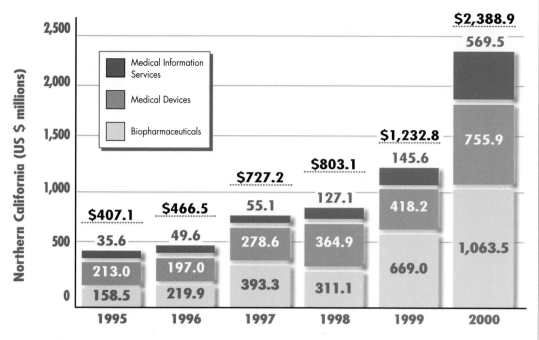

Northern California (US $ millions)

	1995	1996	1997	1998	1999	2000
Total	$407.1	$466.5	$727.2	$803.1	$1,232.8	$2,388.9
Medical Information Services	35.6	49.6	55.1	127.1	145.6	569.5
Medical Devices	213.0	197.0	278.6	364.9	418.2	755.9
Biopharmaceuticals	158.5	219.9	393.3	311.1	669.0	1,063.5

Legend: Medical Information Services, Medical Devices, Biopharmaceuticals

Source: 2002 Report on Northern California's Biomedical R & D Industry, CHI, PricewaterhouseCoopers.

"In the mid-90s, biotech had a down cycle. We had a huge number of clinical failures, and we realized that it would take a long time to produce a drug, as well as a lot of money. We also created more companies than the world could finance, so the industry went through a trough and didn't come out, really, until the announcement of the mapping of the human genome in 1999. And then there was the 2000 boom.

"In the first wave, we were more naive and there was a massive amount of optimism and excitement. It was the kind of industry that everyone loved to see do well because all boats rose with the tide. It was a period of time when everybody cheered for one another, and it was great news to see clinical success."

The upswing

The entire biotech industry was marginalized in the recent bear market; there was much restructuring on Wall Street in 2002. The bankers who used to fund biotech are largely gone. H&Q became JP Morgan; Alex Brown was absorbed by Deutsche Bank; and Montgomery Securities is now part of Banc of America Securities. Biotech banking pioneer Robertson Stephens was acquired by Fleet and then shuttered not long after.

In 2002, some 150 biotech firms raised at least $20 million and some will likely want to float an IPO soon. The big question is, who will slip into the void and take advantage of the enormous opportunity to become the next generation of biotech bankers?

Many believe that it may be tough for companies showing weakness, while solid companies with good stories will continue to get financing. Transactions will occur and the bankers will be there right along with the VCs to finance the next stage of biotech's evolution.

The Bay Area has experienced feast-and-famine periods before. Not only has biotech lived to tell the tale, the industry has flourished. Biotechnology is the one industry that's poised to grapple with major human and environmental challenges, from global hunger to global warming. The industry has moved a long way from the initial mapping of the human genome just two years ago. The industry not only survived the economic challenges of 2002, it moved forward, dramatically breaking new scientific ground in human health-care, diagnostics, agriculture, nutrition, energy, industrial processes and materials, as well as the environment. This is an extraordinary industry that is characterized by long timetables and high financial risk, but investment in biotech is not just about money, it's about humanity, health and the preservation of the planet.

Keeping ALZA Afloat

Martin Gerstel, the founding CFO and long-term CEO of ALZA Corp., saw his company through the best of times and the worst of times. Speaking to a group of biotechnology CEOs at the annual biotech meeting in Laguna Niguel, Gerstel told the saga of ALZA's financing challenges:

One of biotech's greatest success stories is that of Palo Alto-based ALZA Corp. created by Alejandro Zaffaroni in 1968. Zaffaroni was previously president of Syntex Corp., the inventor of the birth-control pill and the hottest company in the United States at the time. In exchange for some licenses to technology, Syntex received 25 percent of ALZA's initial equity, but shortly thereafter distributed all of its ALZA shares to its shareholders as a dividend — one share of ALZA for every 20 shares of Syntex. Thus ALZA became the first publicly traded "venture company" at a time when it had no products in development, no facilities of its own, very few people on staff and almost no capital.

The Pacific Stock Exchange, with only a few listed stocks, decided, without contacting ALZA, to trade the company's shares and arbitrarily opened the market at $10 a share. However, the only shares available in the public market were the limited number of shares being distributed by Syntex to its 20,000 shareholders, and, not surprisingly, most of these people were very interested in buying more; very few were interested in selling the few shares they had received. The price began to skyrocket. Within a few days of the distribution, ALZA's market value was more than $300 million.

Shortly after this, ALZA broke ground for its first offices and research facility in Stanford Research Park. Zaffaroni had to personally guarantee the construction costs. Key scientists were hired as the facilities neared completion.

Soon ALZA began to receive some great publicity. Venture capital was only just beginning. There had not been a new pharmaceutical company established for more than 20 years, and we were creating a company in a most unique manner. For example, *Fortune* magazine's feature story on ALZA was entitled "Visionary on a Golden Shoestring."

In 1971, we had our first public offering for money — a rights offering to our shareholders. This, combined with a private placement, raised $25 million. ALZA was off and running. But after three years of investors "buying the dream," the excitement wore off. We ended 1974 with a very low stock price and only $8 million left.

Things did not look good, but during 1975, marketing requests for our first two products — Ocusert for glaucoma and Progestasert for contraception — were filed with the FDA. The uniqueness of these products again captured the imagination of the financial community. We then obtained an unusual $20 million bank line of credit with no financial covenants and proceeded with a second public offering. This combination provided us with more than $45 million to commercialize Ocusert and Progestasert. By late 1976, both products had been approved and introduced, but a number

Martin Gerstel

of competitive events occurred in 1976 and 1977 that made it difficult for us to successfully market them.

By the end of 1977, ALZA had no money left, owed $20 million under its bank line, was expecting a loss of about $15 million for 1978 and our stock was selling at less than $1 per share. It seemed like the end was near. In early 1978, we entered into a series of agreements with Ciba-Geigy Ltd. whereby they acquired 80 percent voting control of ALZA in the form of a new preferred stock. In this way, Ciba-Geigy was able to utilize our very substantial tax loss without buying any common shares from the public.

For the following five years, ALZA largely disappeared from public view. Then, in early 1982, Ciba-Geigy determined it no longer needed the relationship and could pursue drug delivery on its own, building on the transferred ALZA technologies. Under the 1982 separation agreement, ALZA received a $10 million loan from Ciba-Geigy to allow us to keep the doors open. We immediately sold some real estate to reduce the bank loan to about $8 million and tried to plan for the future. But with less than $10 million in available cash, an ongoing operating loss of more than $10 million a year and a stock value of less than a $1 per share, the future looked extremely bleak.

Our first decision was to concentrate ALZA only on product development, focusing on partnerships with future royalties on successful products. To implement this policy, we said that every R&D activity had to be externally funded by mid-1983 or terminated. This was accomplished, and allowed the survival of the company.

ALZA had a very loyal and committed group of employees, and we decided that extreme measures had to be taken to ensure their continued support. We placed 15 percent of company ownership into an employee stock-ownership plan in the form of a junior stock. There was an important caveat on this arrangement, however, which was that ALZA had to have $4 million in annual earnings for this junior stock to convert to regular common shares. In 1982, this seemed like an impossible dream. As it turned out, the shares converted just two years later.

A key contributor to our rebirth was the commercial introduction in 1983 of Transderm-Nitro®, nitroglycerin in a patch. This product, which ALZA began developing before Ciba-Geigy's controlling acquisition in 1978, was royalty bearing. It ultimately turned a $20 million market into one worth more than $1 billion, bringing ALZA substantial royalties.

By the late 1980s, ALZA had a number of proven drug-delivery platforms, in addition to transdermal methods. Many companies entered into product-development agreements with us. One very important platform was our OROS® osmotic technology for oral delivery, which was the basis for Procardia XL, a heart medication that we developed for Pfizer. It became Pfizer's first-ever billion dollar product.

By pursuing a business model of developing products for other companies at their cost and then sharing in the successes through royalty arrangements, we were able to develop products without our investment or risk. However, our returns from successful products were limited to a 5 to 10 percent royalty. Now, with a multi-billion dollar market cap and nearly a billion dollars in cash, ALZA finally had the resources to return to its original mission of creating a fully integrated pharmaceutical company based on drug delivery.

In 1992, we established a fully owned subsidiary called Therapeutic Discovery Corp. (TDC) and funded it with $250 million of our own cash. TDC entered into agreements to spend the $250 million developing products at ALZA, and ALZA obtained options to both license the products or to buy back TDC. Then we distributed all TDC shares to our shareholders as a dividend, making TDC an entirely independent company from an ownership and accounting standpoint.

By the late 1990s, a number of products initially funded by TDC had been fully developed and approved. ALZA had re-purchased Therapeutic Discovery Corp., had established a capability to market the products in the United States and had successfully commercialized the products. In 2001, Johnson & Johnson acquired ALZA in its largest acquisition ever, for approximately $12 billion. And, today, ALZA continues — under its own name — as a very successful division within that company.

ALZA Headquarters

Shadows and light through an atrium at Mission Bay.

Majed

A Note from an Optimist

by Jean Deleage

It started in 1976. I had the good fortune to share an office with a young investor named Robert Swanson in downtown San Francisco; he had formed Genentech a few months before with a grandiose investment of $200,000. Most of the leading biologists of the time had first met at Asilomar in Pacific Grove and decided that they did not want to do genetic engineering. Professor Herbert Boyer thought differently. Swanson and Boyer were convinced that the benefits of biotechnology for humanity would largely outweigh its

risks, and the risks were, anyway, very controllable. Swanson, who was 28 years old, made it his mission to evangelize the world on the merits of this breakthrough field, and several young scientists broke ranks and followed him. In 1977, and again in 1978, a group of five or six venture capitalists joined Swanson as investors; the cohort of enthusiasts was growing. Swanson made an enthusiast out of me, and, in October 1980, "Genentech Jolts Wall Street," as the *San Francisco Examiner's* front page proclaimed! The stock traded as high as $88 on that first day. It was exciting to hear about the new drugs on the horizon: human growth hormone, TPA and Herceptin®.

In 1980, William J. Rutter and Ed Penhoet came to my office. One week later, Chiron started up in Emeryville. Capital flowed in from different sources. The pharmaceutical industry became an enthusiast and decided to finance several projects; within five years of its inception, Chiron went public.

A little bit later, I became bolder and decided to take a chance on a company addressing central-nervous-system disease with molecules crossing the blood-brain barrier. We searched for a management team capable of success. In the process, we identified Frank Baldino, a young scientist who was also a born entrepreneur. Baldino built Cephalon.

With time, investing became less easy. The multiplication of companies made it more difficult to build perfect teams. Public investors became less eager to invest early, before the materialization of product revenues. Biotechnology management — that unique combination of biologists and venturesome business people — had to worry about chemistry, manufacturing, clinical development and regulatory submission. The Food and Drug Administration (FDA) understood that biotechnology was bringing paradigm changes to the drug industry, and it moved to more tightly channel its activities.

Soon, biotechnology investing became difficult, and often very difficult. But consider the undertaking: Why would it be anything but difficult? As investors, we watch as optimistic scientists wait through FDA trials — Phases I, II and III — of their newly-designed molecular structures. We witness drug failures and successes.

Access to money became cyclical, "windows" opened and closed quickly, and the business model became confusing. Some believed that you had to keep ownership of the drugs to the end, but they did not tell you how to get the money to keep the program moving. Others wanted to partner drugs away at the earliest opportunity, but gave no guidance on how to be successful with no significant product ownership. There was nothing easy about these issues.

In the 1990s, the genome-mapping effort seemed to spark a new birth of the industry. We held our collective breath to see if J. Craig Venter, president of Cetera Genomics, would win the race between public and private companies to map the human genome. New genomics companies were sprouting, and the best scientists were again flocking to these ventures. Rational drug design and the industrialization of research became the accepted paradigm throughout the drug and the biotechnology industry. Investors were once again putting in the financial muscle behind these costly projects, setting the tone for high expectations of quick and extraordinary return.

Alas! When the awaited map of the human genome was completed, some of us were disappointed to learn that we were not much more "gene rich" than a mouse or even the lowly fruit fly. And then it became clear — the decoding of the human genome was only one step in a long and complex process. The logic of moving from gene to druggable target to delivery mechanism was only a very rough sketch. The right and definitive strategy for the discovery of new medicines was not so obvious.

The biotechnology industry is successful because it provides true value. No one can ever argue that there is not value in curing disease, improving human health and enhancing the quality of human life — this is the goal of biotechnology.

Today, important drugs are gaining FDA approval. EPOGEN®, Herceptin® and the hepatitis B vaccine are a few examples. New names are added every year, sometimes leading to new and revolutionary classes of medicines. Notable achievements in recent history include:

- In November 1997, IDEC received FDA approval for Rituxan®, the first genetically engineered monoclonal antibody for treatment of cancer. Sales of Rituxan® exceeded $1 billion in 2002.
- In June 2003, Genentech's Xolair® received FDA approval for the treatment of moderate-to-severe persistent asthma in adults and adolescents.

- In June 2003, the FDA approved MedImmune's FluMist®, the first influenza vaccine delivered as a nasal mist for healthy people.

Pharmaceutical companies have large business-development departments aimed at acquiring or partnering promising discovery-and-development programs conceived by biotechnology companies. In some cases, the in-licensing has become comparable or even bigger than the in-house research and development budget. Pharmaceutical companies are also out-licensing products and programs that the biotechnology companies might handle more successfully.

The industry is now also reveling in the support of the new FDA commissioner, Mark McClellan. In January 2003, McClellan announced an initiative to improve the drug-development regulatory process. In a short amount of time, critical drug candidates have been granted "fast-track" status, new guidelines have been drafted and consideration is being given to the economic risk of delaying drug approvals. Under McClellan's guidance, the FDA is sporting a new attitude of cooperation, communication and efficiency that has greatly invigorated the industry.

For financial investors, biotechnology remains cyclical and somewhat speculative. Regardless, the industry now boasts more than a dozen strongly profitable companies and is an industry that continues to grow in the light of its success. Large acquisitions have occurred — Warner-Lambert/Agouron, Millennium/COR, Amgen/Immunex, Johnson & Johnson/Centocor, Alza and Scios — creating financial successes for the investors. It is generally predicted that this trend will continue, and perhaps accelerate. Furthermore, as of this writing, and despite two years of IPO drought, almost every investment-banking firm is committed to biotechnology. And while leading venture-capital firms have invested consistently, other, less-focused firms have already returned or intend to come back strongly to support the ongoing growth of biotechnology.

Yearly Biotechnology Financing (in millions)

| | U.S. | | | | | Canada |
	2002	2001	2000	1999	1998	2002
IPOs	$456	$208	$4,997	$685	$260	$10
Follow-ons	838	1,695	14,964	3,680	500	186
Other	5,242	3,635	9,987	2,969	787	132
Venture	2,164	2,392	2,773	1,435	1,219	199
Total	**$8,699**	**$7,930**	**$32,722**	**$8,769**	**$2,766**	**$527**

Source: Resilience: America's Biotechnology Report, 2003, Ernst & Young.   Numbers may appear inconsistent because of rounding.

Today, the San Francisco Bay Area biotechnology industry is awash with scientists and executives from Genentech, Chiron and Cetus who have gone on to found and run emerging companies: many of the builders of the initial successful companies now serve on the boards of directors of newer companies in an effort to pass along the wisdom they have acquired through hard work. Leaders and long-time collaborators with biotech companies continue to support their industry by serving as company directors, offering their most valuable gift — their experience. And though many of these people have "retired" at least once, they often return to advise, guide and even lead the companies of tomorrow. When you have been in biotechnology, you stay married to it for life.

NORTHERN CALIFORNIA BIOMEDICAL INDUSTRY
ECONOMIC ACTIVITY

TOTAL BIOMEDICAL COMPANIES: 819

TOTAL REPORTED WORLDWIDE REVENUES: $4.1 BILLION

TOTAL EMPLOYEES: 85,949

TOTAL REPORTED PRIVATE INVESTMENT IN RESEARCH AND DEVELOPMENT: $1.1 BILLION

TOTAL EXPORTS: $2.7 BILLION

TOTAL WAGES AND SALARIES PAID: $5.8 BILLION

TOTAL NIH GRANTS AWARDED: $893 MILLION

Source: "Biomedicine: The New Pillar in Northern California's Economy," CHI/PricewaterhouseCoopers 2002

PROFESSIONAL SERVICES

The Bay Area is home to numerous accounting and consulting firms that assist the biotechnology industry.

Consulting & Accounting Firms Help Shape Bay Area Biotech

by Mike Hildreth and Greg Jensen

The San Francisco Bay Area's fertile business ground produces record numbers of biotechnology companies each year. Many factors contribute to repeated entrepreneurial successes, including the vast network of professional-services firms that gained vital experience from the technology revolution. These firms are applying this expertise to biotechnology.

Accounting and consulting firms have helped shape the Bay Area biotechnology community by providing early-stage companies with advice, guidance and introductions to financing. The firms typically become more involved with these companies as their business functions become more complex, to prepare them for rapid growth. Outsourcing helps early-stage companies leverage the experience of executives who have tackled challenges facing a young company.

The four major players in the accounting world are Ernst & Young, Pricewaterhouse-Coopers, KPMG and Deloitte, as well as a number of regional accounting providers such as Grant Thornton and BDO Seidman. Partnering with these organizations has become standard operating procedure for early-stage biotech companies. The Bay Area also has many chief financial officer (CFO) outsourcing agencies, such as Ravix Group Inc., David Powell Inc., Square One Finance, CFOs2GO.com and Horn Murdock Cole, which have played a vital role.

Many additional consulting groups provide services that span beyond a company's financial needs. For example, PRTM, Cap Gemini Ernst & Young, Deloitte Consulting, BearingPoint, Mackenzie and Accenture are more involved with later-stage companies, providing business strategy, marketing, product development and corporate development. Other groups provide services such as technology transfer or clinical-trial designs for early-stage companies that do not have the internal resources to perform these functions, which ultimately save the company money and time.

In the Bay Area, life-science professional-services firms employ approximately 25,000 people. Business-service firms typically serve all sizes of companies, from the classic garage startup to those with approximately $10 million in funding to the largest public companies. The partners of these firms invest time in the early-stage companies with a vision — that their early investment that will pay off when the company becomes a market leader and enters the public market, providing the firm with a loyal client for years to come.

Accounting firms provide basic audit and tax services to early-stage companies. As the companies grow, they provide additional services to help them prepare for an initial public offering (IPO), support transactions and support increasing corporate-governance demands of public companies. Following an IPO, accounting firms continue to provide audit and tax services, but may also provide additional financial-systems implementation, treasury services, real-estate advisory services and transaction support services. When an accounting firm does not serve as the auditor, the scope of services it is able to perform is not restricted under Sarbanes Oxley legislation and the firm is able to provide internal audit functions, in addition to many other business and finance-related services.

Consulting firms, on the other hand, focus on projects that accounting firms do not typically provide. These projects can be wide ranging, from strategic consulting to product development to corporate development. Accounting firms began to divest of their consulting practices five years ago to more clearly delineate consulting from accounting services and remove any semblance of conflict of interest.

Consulting and accounting firms will often meet with newly formed companies to discuss the growing company's plans and to provide limited free advice. Their professional-service teams assist the new companies with business-plan development, introduce them to the venture community, provide timely advice and help them participate in industry events. These firms also have valuable connections with seasoned technology-transfer teams at universities and large, successful biotech companies in the area. These connections can be integral to the success of an early-stage company.

Accounting and consulting firms also sponsor meetings during which start-up companies can refine or build a business plan and put their message in front of investors. These forums gather consulting groups, accountants, banks and venture capitalists (VCs) in a setting that allows companies at the earliest stage of formation to brainstorm ideas with tenured executives. There is no fee, and the consulting firms help the startups create the proper foundation to build a successful business. Early coaching can lead to introductions to VCs and enable companies to set a proven, sound foundation for growing their business. A solid foundation aids the entire biotechnology industry because it prepares entrepreneurs to avoid the pitfalls that may prove costly later in the business cycle.

Most consulting and accounting firms recognize the value of maintaining good relationships with VC firms, financial institutions and other service providers. VCs pay attention to specific types of technology. Knowing what is hot can influence the strategy of consulting firms and the services they offer. Frequently, VC firms contact the accountants and consultants they know to provide services to their portfolio

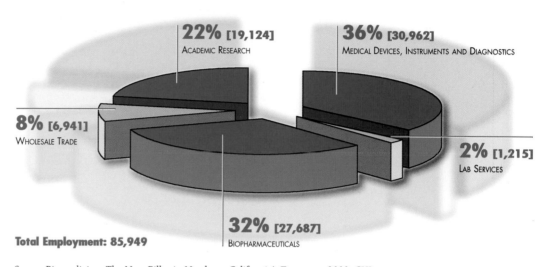

Distribution of Jobs in Northern California's Biomedical Industry, 2000

22% [19,124] ACADEMIC RESEARCH

36% [30,962] MEDICAL DEVICES, INSTRUMENTS AND DIAGNOSTICS

8% [6,941] WHOLESALE TRADE

2% [1,215] LAB SERVICES

32% [27,687] BIOPHARMACEUTICALS

Total Employment: 85,949

Source: Biomedicine: The New Pillar in Northern California's Economy, 2000, CHI

companies. This is done through a variety of means. Some consulting firms set up formal meetings with the VCs; others maintain contact through joint sponsorship of industry conferences.

Industry organizations are well supported by consulting and accounting firms, provided they are established and offer high-level content that interests executives and entrepreneurs. Professional-services firms typically use industry events to network, learn about new businesses, communicate new service offerings and demonstrate industry expertise through participation on panels and speeches. In the Bay Area, every major biotech industry organization has a presence.

INDUSTRY ORGANIZATION	FOCUS	WEBSITE
Biotechnology Industry Organization	National lobby for entire biotech industry	www.bio.org
Bay Area Bioscience (BayBIO)	California lobby for biotech legal issues, events and strategic planning, networking with research institutions	www.baybio.org
BioE2E	Entrepreneurial services to biotech startup companies	
Biospace	Industry Information (companies, jobs, events, stock quotes, industry news and paid databases)	www.biospace.com
Mission Bay	Human capital, company incubation, technology development, lab space	
California Healthcare Institute (CHI)	Healthcare and life-sciences companies	www.chi.org

The Bay Area provides fertile ground for the successful development of biotechnology companies. Professional-service firms play an important role. Service firms have learned and gained valuable insight from helping to form hundreds of successful technology and biotech companies. This expertise provides early-stage companies with resources that surpass those found in any other area of the world.

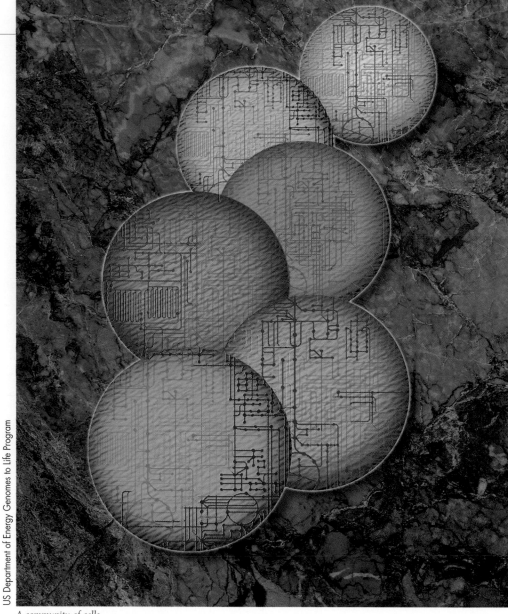

US Department of Energy Genomes to Life Program

A community of cells.

Bay Area Biotech and the Legal Industry

by Kenneth E. Jenkins, Kathryn J. Mengerink and Jeffry S. Mann

Since 1976 when Genentech was established in the Bay Area, the region has witnessed tremendous growth in the biotechnology industry. According to a recent survey by Ernst & Young, there are currently 68 publicly held biotechnology companies in the Bay Area, employing approximately 35,000 people.[1] Other sources, such as the Bay Area Bioscience Center (BayBio) counted 800 total biotechnology companies in the Bay Area in 2002, employing some 85,000 people.[2] This represents a greater than seven-fold increase since 1987, when 112 companies inhabited the Bay Area, providing 19,400 jobs.

As the biotechnology industry has grown, patent law and patent practitioners have continued to develop approaches to address new challenges presented by emerging biotechnologies. The changes in patent law, coupled with the increasingly complex biotechnology industry, has challenged the legal community, including the courts, the patent office, patent litigators and patent prosecutors, to extend and intensify their understanding of both law and science.

Changes in patent law
have contributed to the growth of biotechnology

The United States Constitution grants Congress the power to "promote the Progress of Science and useful Arts, by securing for a limited time to Authors and Inventors the exclusive Right to their respective Writings and Discoveries." [3] Congress has established a system of patent laws that allows a patent owner to prevent others from making, using or selling the owner's patented invention. In exchange for a monopoly on the patented invention for 20 years from the date of filing, the public gains the benefit of the teachings that the inventor is required to disclose. The 20-year patent monopoly is especially important in the biotechnology industry, where companies must recoup the high costs of research necessary to develop an invention and bring a product based upon the invention to market.[4] Biotechnology companies have utilized the patent system from the very beginning, as exemplified by the famous Cohen-Boyer patent for the invention of recombinant DNA cloning.[5] This invention led to the creation of Genentech by inventor Herbert Boyer and business-partner Robert Swanson.[6]

To obtain a patent, the claimed invention must, at minimum, be novel, non-obvious, useful and encompass appropriate subject matter.[7] As the number of biotechnology patent applications increases, courts continue to refine the requirements for the patentability of an invention in order to address emerging technologies. A few of the key court decisions elucidating the standards of patentability of biotechnology inventions are discussed below.

Patentable subject matter

Under 35 U.S.C. § 101 of the Patent Act, courts have traditionally excluded "laws of nature, physical phenomena and abstract ideas" from the category of patentable subject matter.[8,9] During the last century, the courts have attempted to clarify the scope of patentable subject matter in the field of life sciences.

In the early part of the 20th century, courts addressed the status of natural products isolated from biological sources. For example, in *Parke-Davis & Co. v. H. K. Mulford & Co.*, the Court of the Southern District of New York addressed whether a biological compound purified from its source is patentable.[10] The invention at issue was drawn to a stable form of adrenaline purified from the adrenal glands.[11] In holding that the purified adrenaline was patentable subject matter under § 101, the court attempted to distinguish purified adrenaline from adrenaline in its natural state. The court reasoned that the purified adrenaline was "for every practical purpose a new thing commercially and therapeutically . . . not merely the old dried glands in a purer state."[12]

In 1947, the United States Supreme Court examined the scope of 35 U.S.C. § 101 in *Funk Bros. Seed Co. v. Kalo Inoculant Co.*[13] The invention was a mixture of isolated microbes useful for inoculating leguminous plants.[14] Prior to the invention, only single strains of microbes were used to inoculate leguminous plants.[15] The Supreme Court held that the mixed culture of microbes was not patentable subject matter because the bacteria were "manifestations of laws of nature, free to all men and reserved exclusively to none."[16]

Whether micro-organisms were patentable remained unclear until 1980, when the Supreme Court revisited the issue in *Diamond v. Chakrabarty*.[17] The invention was bacteria genetically altered to express enzymes capable of degrading oil.[18] The Supreme Court held the organisms to be patentable because they were "a product of human ingenuity."[19] The Court distinguished *Funk Brothers*, reasoning that a recombinant microbe cannot be found in nature, whereas the inherent characteristics of the microbes in *Funk Brothers* remained unaltered.[20] The Court famously proclaimed that "anything under the sun that is made by man" is patentable subject matter.[21] This monumental decision further opened the doors for patenting in the field of biotechnology. In the same year that the Supreme Court decided Chakrabarty, the Bay Area's Genentech became the first biotechnology company to go public.[22]

In the wake of *Chakrabarty*, courts addressed the patentability of complex multi-cellular organisms.[23] For example, in *Ex Parte Allen* (1987), the Board of Patent Appeals and Interferences stated that a genetically modified oyster (having multiple genome copies) was patentable subject matter. The board reasoned that the standard for patentability under § 101 was not whether the subject matter composed "living entities" but "simply whether

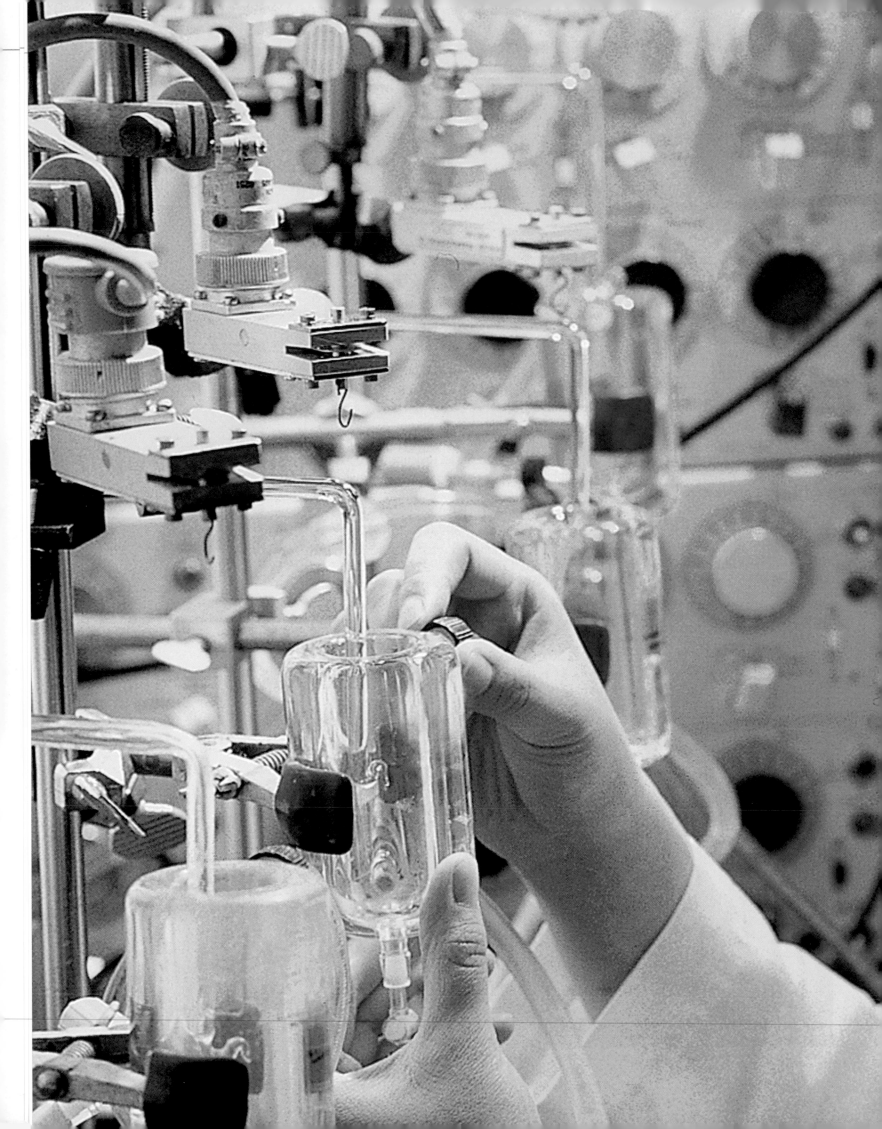

DRUG DEVELOPMENT & DELIVERY

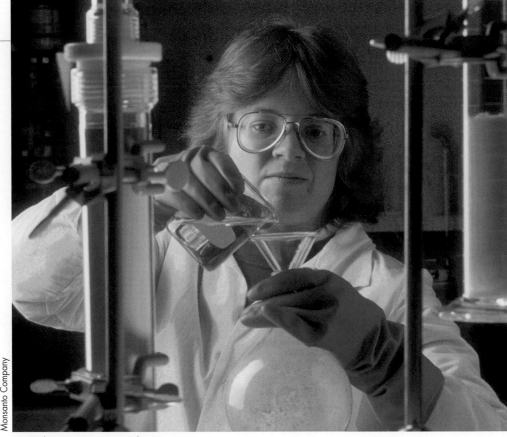

Monsanto Company

Research requires precision and concentration.

The Business of Biotech — Product Development Cycles

by Cynthia Robbins-Roth

The drug development process: test tubes to patients

For any biotechnology or pharmaceutical company, the driver of both opportunity and risk is product development. All of the exciting science in the world will not generate long-term value, unless it is used to create products that bring a significant revenue stream into the company.

This process — and the associated risk — is essentially identical for small biotech companies and for large pharmaceutical firms. The key difference is that big pharma has ongoing product revenues to cushion the inevitable product failure, and often does not have to reveal when those failures occur. If the company is large enough, and the failure early enough, it is not a reportable event as defined by the US Securities and Exchange Commission (SEC). Unfortunately, most biotech firms do not have that luxury. Every product candidate is crucial to their success, and any speed bump must be reported.

Drug discovery

The discovery and development of a new pharmaceutical is a long and arduous task. According to the Tufts Center for the Study of Drug Development, it takes an average of 15 years for a new drug to move from the discovery phase, into animal testing, through clinical trials, past the US Food and Drug Administration (FDA) and into the marketplace. The average cost of generating a single new drug is an estimated $500 million or more.

The scariest part is the risk. Estimates from the Pharmaceutical Research and Manufacturers of America say that for every 5,000 compounds that emerge from discovery and make it to animal testing (termed preclinical testing), only about five compounds perform well enough to move on into human testing. And only one of those five makes it into the marketplace.

Even market launch does not guarantee continued success. A candidate compound drug can make it all the way through the clinical and regulatory maze, reap kudos from Wall Street analysts and high-profile physicians, and still hit unexpected road blocks in the real world of the marketplace.

While drugs aimed at newly discovered mechanisms of disease show the greatest promise of solving previously unsolved health problems, there are often unexpected toxic side-effects that show up only in later stages of clinical testing — or later. If you are lucky, the product will be a survivor and earn back the $500+ million the company spent to develop it.

Rewards

So why get involved in this game at all? Two key reasons: 1) the opportunity to hit the jackpot — the drug that generates $1 billion or more each year in sales revenues; and 2) the chance to make a real difference to patients.

No company — not even the big pharma pros — can accurately predict how a compound will do in development. Even once a product hits the market, unexpected issues can affect its performance. No drug is a completely innocuous entity; every drug has adverse effects of some kind. The trick of clinical development is to show that the benefits outweigh the perils. The trick of marketing is to grow the market as large as possible without recruiting patients who will suffer toxic side effects that may endanger the product for everyone.

Let's take a closer look at the stages of drug development — what happens at each step, and where things can go awry.

Stages of Drug Development

Stage	Early Research/ Preclinical Testing	Phase I: Clinical Trials	Phase II	Phase III	FDA Review Process/Approval	On Market	Phase IV
Years	6.5	1.5	2	3.5	1.5	Took 15 years to get here	
Test Population	Test tube and animal studies	20 to 80 healthy volunteers	100 to 300 patients	1,000 to 3,000 patients			Patients
Purpose	Look for safety, desired activity	Determine safety and dosage for the next phase	Evaluate effectiveness, look for potential toxic side effects	Confirm effectiveness, look for side effects from long-term use			Post-marketing surveillance of the patients to look for potential problems
Success Rate	5,000 evaluated	5 compounds enter clinical trials			1 compound approved		

Sources: San Francisco Business Journal *and* Burrill & Company.

Discovery and early research

The biotech industry has shown itself to be extremely adept at creating new ways to support the very front end of the process — discovery. In fact, the industry has become so successful at this stage that most large pharmaceutical companies devote a hefty share of their R&D budget (up to 50 percent) to supporting research originating with their smaller biotech brethren.

The key to discovery is using the biotech tools of molecular biology, cell biology, assay development, combinatorial chemistry and high-throughput screening to probe the inner workings of cells and decipher just what is causing disease. Each new wave of technology advancement allows scientists to dive more deeply and specifically into the molecular and cellular interactions that cause the outer signs of diseases.

In the past, researchers and physicians often did not know what was causing the symptoms they were trying to treat. The result was that most drugs were aimed at symptoms, for example, the pain, inflammation and swelling of arthritis, without touching the basic cause of the disease — a chain of cell interactions that causes the chronic release of enzymes and other molecules that chew up joints and cause the symptoms. This meant that the disease often was never cured.

New tools and technologies help researchers identify specific "targets" to go after with drugs. In the case of arthritis, the target might be the gene encoding an enzyme that destroys joint cartilage or the protein used by immune-system cells in the joint to recruit other inflammatory cells to come join the party and cause more damage. Once a disease-specific target is found, scientists can look for chemical structures that can change the behavior of the target and stop the disease process.

Typically, hundreds or thousands of chemical structures are tested for their ability to act on the disease target in a test tube or in individual cells (termed tissue culture) — in other words, whether they are "hits" or "misses."

These simple systems have fewer variables than a whole animal. The good news is that this makes it easier to see if the compound works. The bad news is that a compound can work at this level, but have properties that prevent it from working properly in a whole animal.

Sometimes compounds can act directly on a target in a test tube, but cannot make their way through the membrane that surrounds the cell containing the target. Sometimes enzymes in the blood chew the compounds up so quickly that they do not last long enough to act on the target. Often, a compound is simply not potent enough — patients would have to consume pounds of the stuff to get the therapeutic benefit. It is sometimes possible to tinker with a promising, but impotent, compound and crank up the potency or fix some of the other characteristics that otherwise would keep it in the "failure" bin. This is why animal testing is crucial — only in a whole, living animal can the compound's characteristics be fully tested.

Preclinical testing

Once a lead compound emerges from research, it's time to see if it works in whole animals — an exponential leap in complexity. Preclinical testing involves a series of tests in animals and laboratories to generate data that will convince the FDA that it is safe and worthwhile to try the drug candidate in people. The tests also help determine how to give the drug to people so that it is most likely to work.

These tests are aimed at determining what happens when a whole animal metabolizes the drug: Are toxic metabolites created? Does the drug lose its effectiveness? What doses generate the desired effects, what doses cause toxicity? How fast does the drug disappear from the blood, and where does it go? Can the drug be given as a pill without losing its effectiveness through digestion in the stomach, or is injection required? Does the formulation need to be changed from intravenous injection to subcutaneous or to an inhaled version? Does the drug have any unexpected activities? Does it affect fetal development or pregnancy? There are studies that test what happens when an animal is treated for up to a year to look for effects from chronic exposure.

In some cases, when a drug will be used to treat a chronic disease — one that lasts for years rather than weeks — animal studies lasting up to two years may be required to study effects of chronic exposure and to look for potential cancer-causing effects.

An important issue is how selective a "hit" is. A compound that has the desired effect on the disease target, but which also affects the behavior of other molecules in the body is not a good drug candidate. The lack of selectivity can lead to nasty side effects by harming healthy cells in the body. A classic example of this lack of selectivity is seen in most cancer chemotherapy drugs. These drugs kill rapidly dividing cells — like cancer cells. Unfortunately, other cells that normally divide rapidly include the cells lining the gut, hair follicles and the bone marrow cells that produce red and white blood cells. This is why cancer patients often lose their hair and become anemic during treatment.

Preclinical studies also are used to generate information about how to calculate the dose that should be used in the clinical studies. It is necessary to determine the largest dose that can be given to an animal before toxic side effects begin to show up. If that maximum tolerated dose is too close to the dose required to generate an effective therapeutic response (termed a narrow therapeutic window), the drug candidate may be dropped as too risky.

Peg Skorpinski

Boris Stoeber (right) gently presses the MEMS chiclet on Dorian Liepmann's hand, all it takes to deliver a life-saving dose of antibiotics. Stoeber fabricated the 10 mm x 10 mm MEMS syringe. Prototype in the Berkeley Microfabrication Lab, a project funded by the Defense Research Projects Agency and Becton, Dickinson and Company.

Some development programs are complicated by the lack of animal models for the human disease being studied. For example, animals cannot be infected by the virus that causes AIDS. This forced researchers to work with related viruses — simian AIDS in monkeys and the version that infects cats.

While it's possible to draw parallels between the human and animal systems, there are many differences. Often, there are slight differences in the proteins used by humans and animals to carry out the same activity. This can mean that a compound that works in animals might not work the same, or as well, in humans.

There has been great progress in developing tissue-based assay systems that resemble human organs — skin, corneas, kidneys — to use in testing and perhaps to replace some of the animal testing required today. However, even though the cells being used are human, there is no replacement for testing in living patients. Other systems can only give us hints about how the drug might work and how it should be given to increase the chance of success.

It can take three to four years of testing at this level to generate the information required by the FDA. Usually this same information is required by the other key regulatory agencies around the world before clinical studies can begin in other countries.

Along with the animal studies to understand how the drug works, the company needs to conduct studies of the drug compound itself — how long is it stable at different temperatures (room temperature, refrigerated, frozen); what form (dry powder, ready-to-use injectable, pill or tablet) is best; and how to manufacture reproducible batches over time. Manufacturing and drug-property issues could knock a drug contender out just as readily as efficacy issues. If the company cannot make the drug at a cost that allows reasonable profit without pricing the product too high for the market, or if it needs to be injected and its competition is a once-daily pill, the product will have a tough time competing in the marketplace.

Clinical trials: a work in progress

Clinical trials are the studies done in humans — healthy volunteers and patients with the target disease — to test whether the drug candidate works in people. Actually, it's far more complicated than that. It's not just a question of whether the drug works or not. The data also must address:

- whether the drug works well enough to be worth giving to patients;
- whether the potential risk of toxic side effects outweighs the therapeutic benefit;
- which dose regimen (daily, 2X daily, weekly, given for how long, given via which route — injection, orally, inhaled, sustained release formulation) provides the best response and least amount of side effects;
- whether the drug is better than, equivalent to, or worse than existing treatments for the disease.

In today's managed health-care environment, where insurers essentially decide which drugs are used by controlling which drugs they will pay for, companies must build into their clinical trials a way to determine the cost/benefit ratio for a new treatment. In other words, even if the drug works, it must provide sufficient benefit to support the cost or else must make the total cost of care lower (perhaps through reducing the number of days a patient spends in the intensive care unit). This is termed pharmacoeconomic analysis.

Peg Skorpinski

This neon-lit, transparent microfluidic device, seen here on an inverted stage microscope, allows Stoeber to visualize the route particles travel as they enter a small channel, much like the microneedle channels in in the chiclet-sized syringe.

Phase I

Phase I studies are designed primarily to look at safety in humans, and to study how the drug is metabolized and where it goes in the human body. Phase I will also provide important information to guide design of dosing for the later clinical phases, especially in terms of limiting nasty side effects. These trials usually involve 20 to 80 healthy volunteers or patients treated with increasingly high doses, covering doses all the way from no possible effect to potentially toxic. The number of volunteers used in these studies depends on how many doses are tested, and if the study design needs to examine issues such as the impact of taking the drug on an empty stomach or after a meal.

The goal of Phase I studies is not to assess the drug candidate's effectiveness, but rather to gain hints about the best way to use the product and whether it is safe to use in people. The information is used to design the Phase II studies.

Phase II

This phase of clinical development is designed to provide more information about how the drug behaves in people and to begin providing information about effectiveness in patients. These studies typically include 100 to 500 patients, divided into several different subgroups. The subgroups are given the drug in different doses, different routes

Biopharmaceutical Funding by Region

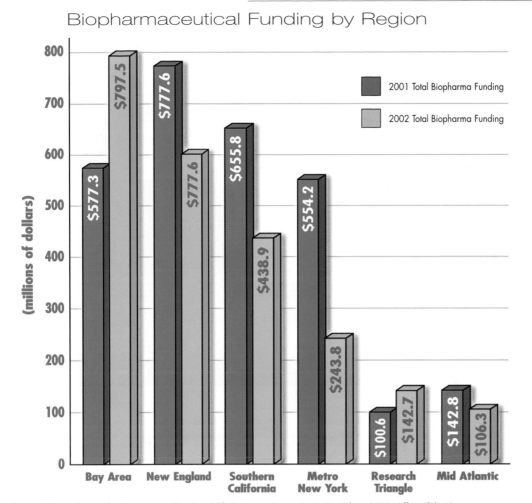

Source: Taking Action for Tomorrow: Bay Area Life Sciences Strategic Action Plan, *2003, Office of the Governor, Bay Area Council, Monitor Group.*

(intravenous vs. subcutaneous, for example) and on different schedules (twice daily for two weeks vs. four times daily, for example).

Sometimes, parallel Phase II trials are run in different patient subpopulations. For example, in cancer trials, companies may run trials in patients with breast, ovarian, renal and prostate cancer to see if the drug is broadly useful or if it seems to be more effective in certain cancers. This information allows design of Phase III trials that focus on those patients most likely to be able to respond well to the treatment.

In any case, more than one Phase II study is typically required to gather all of the necessary information for optimal Phase III design. The Phase II results will allow companies to understand more thoroughly how their drug works in something more closely resembling the "real world," and to hone in on the best combination of dose, treatment schedule and patient subpopulation likely to respond to the drug. Safety issues continue to be important. Phase II trials will not provide definitive proof of effectiveness.

Phase III

The role of Phase III trials, sometimes called pivotal trials, is to generate data that will lead FDA and the international regulatory-agencies to give the company permission to market its new drug. Building on the hints about effectiveness, patient sub-populations, dosing regimens and pharmacoeconomic issues, the company is hoping to end up with statistically significant proof that its product candidate is effective enough — and safe enough — to warrant use.

The drug division of FDA, in charge of small-molecule drugs, typically requires two Phase III trials before considering a New Drug Application (NDA). The exceptions are for drugs aimed at life-threatening diseases where no effective treatment exists, or where the candidate drug may reduce the death rate. However, in these cases, the FDA wants a more careful evaluation of the drug after approval and frequently asks for a number of post-marketing studies as a condition of approval.

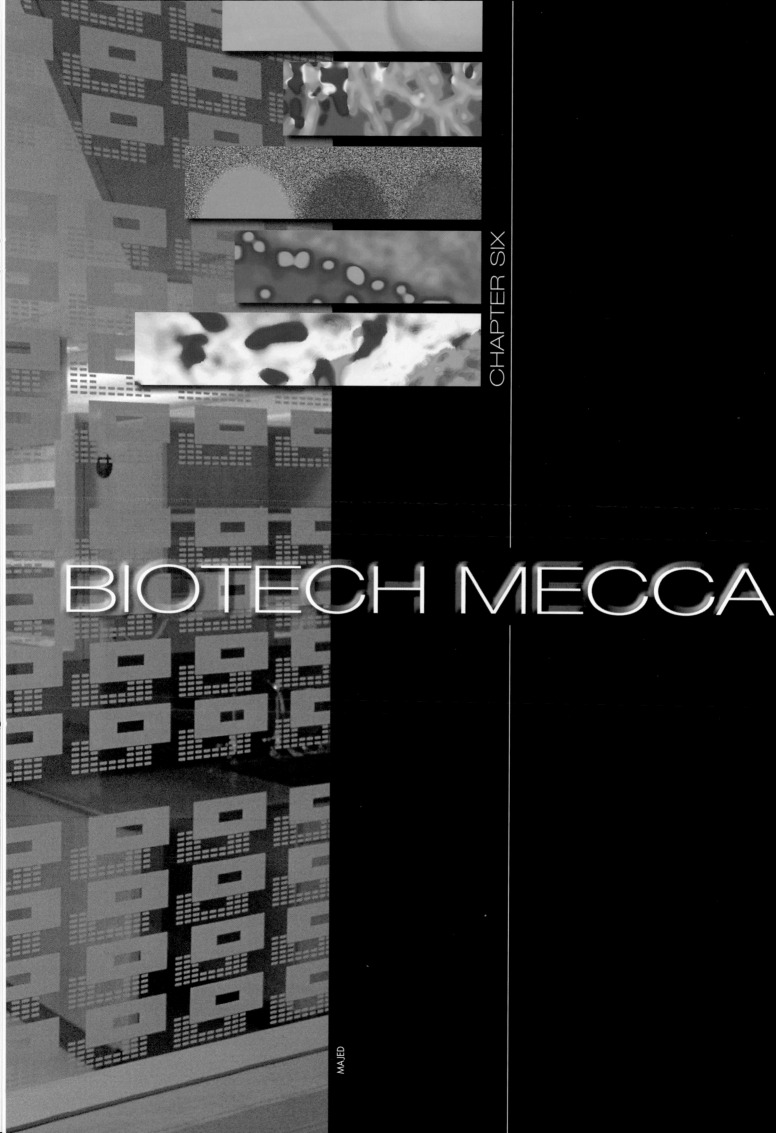

CHAPTER SIX

BIOTECH MECCA

MAJED

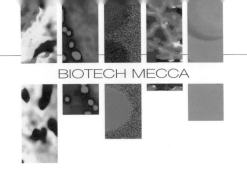

Biotech Bay

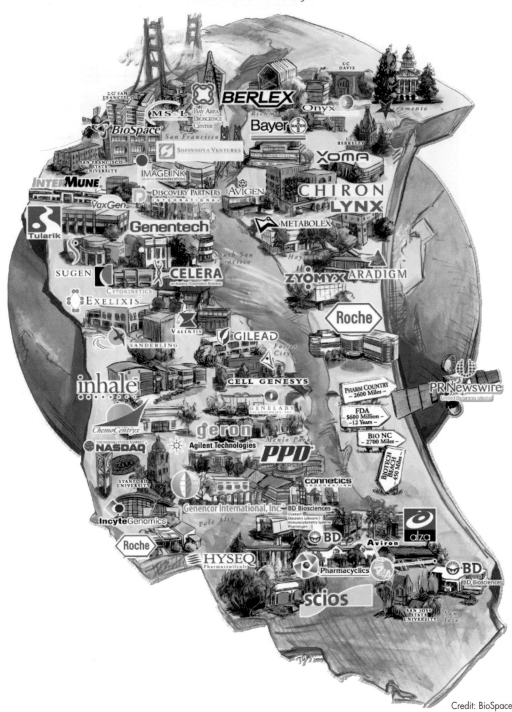

Credit: BioSpace

Sub-clusters

The Bay Area region, which covers 7,000 square miles around the San Francisco Bay, consists of nine counties: Alameda, Contra Costa, Marin, Napa, San Francisco, San Mateo, Santa Clara, Solano and Sonoma. Nearly one-fifth of the people in California live in this region — approximately 7 million people.

The public biotech companies of this area employ more than 31,000 of the nearly 80,000 people who are directly employed by public and private biotech companies. According to a 2003 report by the Bay Area Strategic Plan, *Taking Action for Tomorrow*, nearly $2 billion in wages are generated by this sector. When government-backed research institutions, educational institutions, service providers and biotech-research facilities owned by pharmaceutical companies are included, the number of people employed in this industry reaches nearly 200,000. A number of sub-clusters thriving in the Bay Area contain high concentrations of biotech companies, namely South San Francisco, the Peninsula, the South Bay, East Bay and North Bay.

Bay Area Sub Cluster Distribution

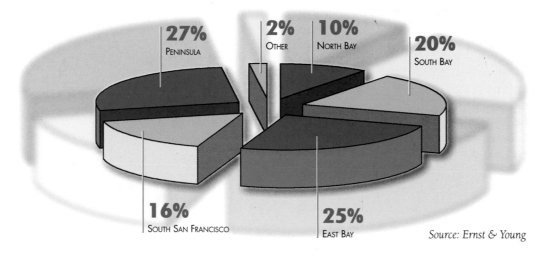

27% PENINSULA

2% OTHER

10% NORTH BAY

20% SOUTH BAY

16% SOUTH SAN FRANCISCO

25% EAST BAY

Source: Ernst & Young

The East Bay cluster is primarily focused in Emeryville, Berkeley, Alameda, Danville, Pleasanton and Fremont. Driven by innovative technology from UC Berkeley, the Ernest Orlando Lawrence Berkeley National Laboratory (Berkeley Lab) and the Lawrence Livermore National Laboratory, the East Bay is home to the second-largest sub-cluster in the Bay Area by the number of companies and revenues generation, or market cap. Many areas of this region are attracting new companies and subsidiaries of large public companies, due to the lower cost of living and doing business than other Bay Area locations. The East Bay cluster is made up of a few concentrations of companies primarily in the Fremont and Emeryville/Berkeley area. UC Berkeley has been the source of innovative technology and new company formation, as well as providing the expected trained personnel to manage companies. Chiron in Emeryville has been the marquis company of this sub-cluster, and the region has the second-highest market cap and percentage of companies.

South San Francisco has the distinction of being home to Genentech and has seen many companies form in that area from the innovations and talent developed by Genentech. This sub-cluster leads the Bay Area in market cap. The area has benefited from the technology transfer of UCSF and will undoubtedly grow from the close proximity of the Mission Bay project as scientists and companies begin to locate there.

A number of VC funds have primary offices in South San Francisco, in San Francisco and in the nearby Peninsula sub-cluster, making access to capital and working with venture capitalists convenient. Genentech is one of the few biotech companies with a venture fund.

The Peninsula cluster has a higher concentration of VC firms than anywhere in the world. This cluster has a highly developed network of business-services companies and small, consulting businesses that assist in the development of early-stage companies. Stanford University has a leading technology-transfer office that has continued to lead to formation of many life-sciences companies. Stanford has also been the source of experienced people who are critical to the success of the companies formed to commercialize new technology. The Peninsula has the highest percentage of companies in the area and is home to many companies that are in the top tier of the industry. Gilead is the most notable, with its success in the last few years and innovative leadership.

Technology has made a great impact on the South Bay sub-cluster. The first companies to take technology from Silicon Valley and translate the technology into tremendous tools of discovery in biotech came from this sub-cluster. Affymetrix gene chips directly merged the silicon wafer with genome sequencing. This is only the beginning, however, and many companies in this sub-cluster have benefited from advances in the technology industry.

In the North Bay, there is a large variety of companies focused on everything from developing discovery tools for biotechnology companies to classic biopharmaceutical companies, such as BioMarin in Novato. This area has the added advantage of a more reasonable cost of living and doing business, and will likely see more biotech companies locate to this area as a result.

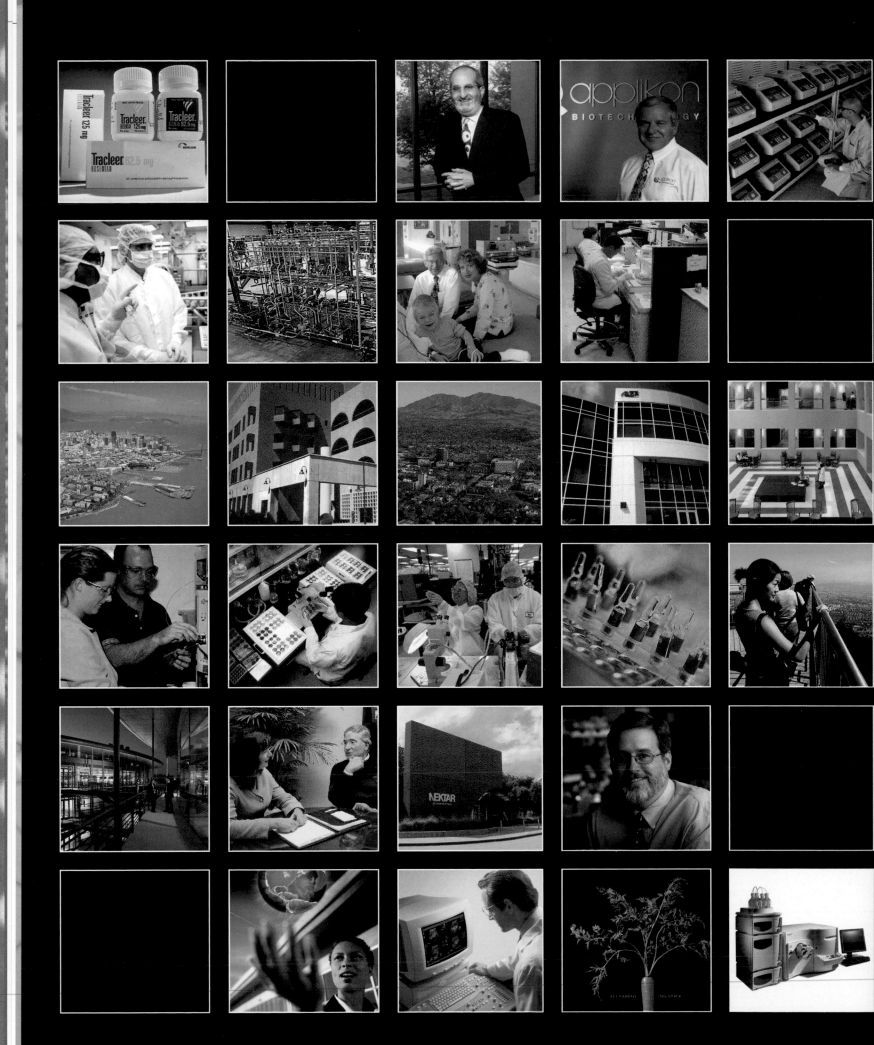

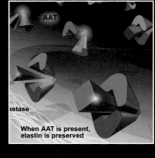

CHAPTER EIGHT

When AAT is present, elastin is preserved

PROFILES OF EXCELLENCE

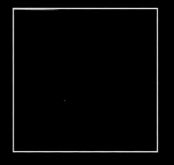

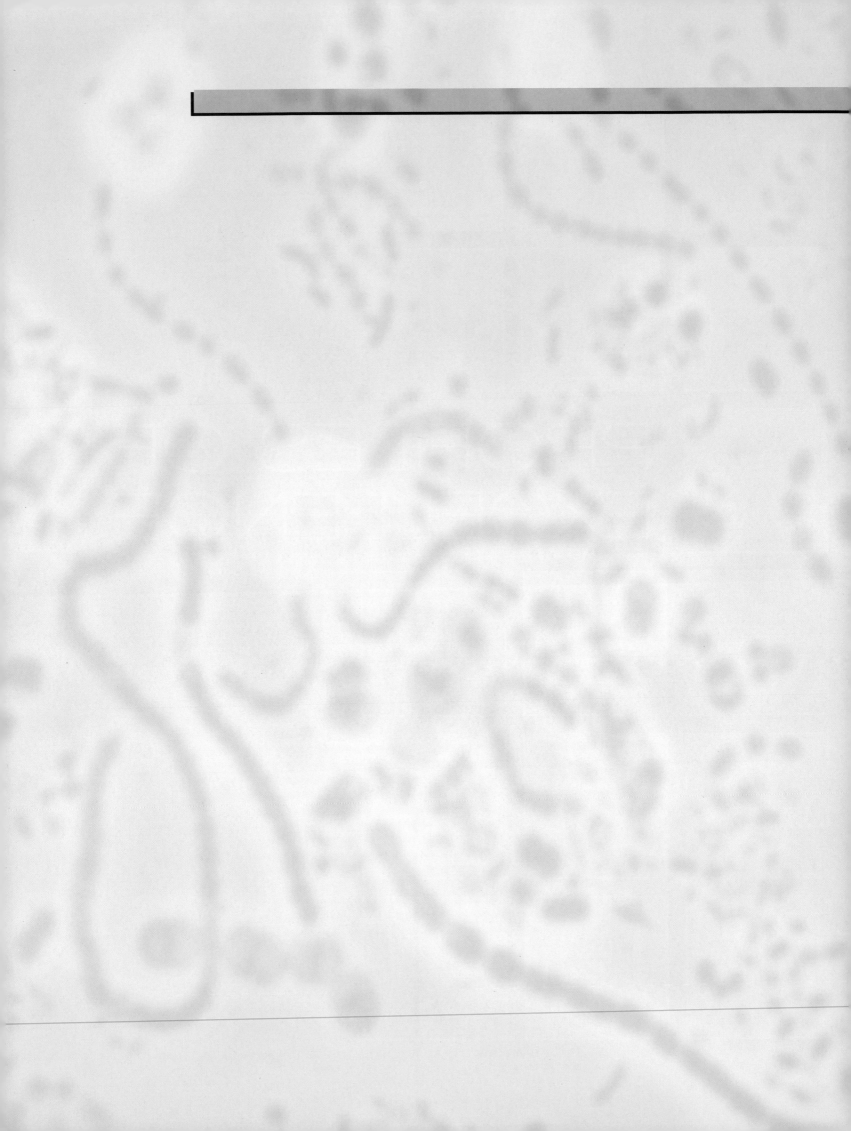

Profiles of Excellence

Actelion

Founded in 1997 in Basel, Switzerland, Actelion Ltd. is one of the fastest growing biopharmaceutical companies in the world. Based on the strength of its first product, Tracleer®, in just a few short years the company has grown to employ more than 500 worldwide in drug research and development, sales and marketing. Tracleer® is the world's first oral treatment for the deadly disease, pulmonary arterial hypertension. In this disease, high levels of a substance in the body called endothelin cause blood vessels in the lung to close down and scar, leading to high blood pressure and ultimately heart failure.

"Tracleer® is the first oral endothelin antagonist," says Simon Buckingham, president of Actelion Pharmaceuticals US. "It blocks the harmful effects of endothelin and has been a godsend for people with this disease."

Tracleer® received orphan drug status and a rapid approval by the US Food and Drug Administration. For many patients suffering pulmonary arterial hypertension, Tracleer®, an oral tablet, represents an important alternative to chronic infusion therapy.

The past year has been a busy one, as Actelion celebrated the successful launch of Tracleer® in Canada, Europe, the United States and Switzerland. Actelion intends to launch Tracleer® in Israel, Australia and Japan in 2003.

Actelion chose the Bay Area to establish its US headquarters back in the year 2000. "The Bay Area is the cradle of US biotechnology, where this industry started, and where we can find top people in any discipline," Dr. Buckingham says.

The spirit of entrepreneurial and scientific innovation that helped propel the company in its inception permeated the culture of Actelion, and will propel the growing company to profitability in the near term.

"Success depends on a lot of factors, but it often boils down to getting two things right," Dr. Buckingham explains. "You need good products, and you need to have great people. If you have those, then you've got the primary building blocks for success. Our simple, open and innovative culture is a critical part of our success, as is our burning desire to develop drugs that really change people's lives."

And if past success is any indication, Tracleer® is only the beginning of an innovative therapeutic science using the endothelium, and Actelion is well on its way toward building a biopharmaceutical powerhouse.

The inner lining of blood vessels is a single layer of cells, known collectively as the endothelium. These cells cover every surface that comes into contact with blood, forming a thin protective layer to prevent the clotting of the blood, regulating formation of new blood vessels and blood flow. Problems with the endothelium have been associated with common diseases, such as heart failure, artherosclerosis and other disorders.

Actelion continues to investigate the Tracleer® for new indications including scleroderma, metastatic melanoma and interstitial lung disease.

"Our research and development is focused on the endothelium as a target for discovery of drugs," Dr. Buckingham says. "Our vision is that this approach can provide new therapies and hope for those suffering from other debilitating and as-yet-untreatable diseases."

Actelion has also initiated late stage clinical trials in Acute Heart Failure with its second drug, Veletri™, another endothelin antagonist. If successful, it plans to co-market this product with Bay Area neighbor, Genentech. Additional early stage research projects aim to find inhibitors or antagonists of other harmful substances such as orexin, implicated in eating and sleeping disorders and renin, a target with an important role in cardiovascular disease.

"We are all about finding drugs that make a difference for patients," Dr. Buckingham says. ■

Actelion Pharmaceuticals US Inc.
601 Gateway Blvd., Ste. 100
South San Francisco, CA 94080
www.actelion.com

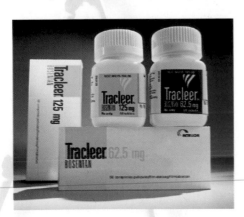

Alta Partners

With a portfolio that has included 85 of the leading life-sciences companies since 1996, Alta Partners is considered one of the leading venture capital firms in the Bay Area.

Alta Partners was founded by four senior partners of Burr, Egan, Deleage & Co. (BEDCO), a premier venture capital firm formed in 1979. Jean Deleage, a founder of BEDCO and Alta Partners, was one of the first venture capitalists to invest in both Bay Area biotech giants, Genentech and Chiron. Such cornerstone investments provided the basis for Alta's subsequent growth and success in the Bay Area.

Alta's status as a preferred venture partner nationwide is based on its commitment to the life sciences and to the quality of its team of investment professionals. Today, Alta's investment team consists of 14 individuals with decades of venture capital, operating, clinical and investment banking experience. This wealth and diversity of expertise provides Alta with a significant advantage in evaluating potential portfolio companies, as well as assisting these companies in achieving operating success. While the firm is committed to only investing in those areas where it possesses specific domain knowledge, its broad in-house expertise allows the team to pursue and support opportunities across a significant segment of the life sciences industry.

Alta Partners currently manages five venture funds, aggregating approximately $1 billion in committed capital, and takes a comprehensive approach to investing in life sciences. Whereas traditional venture firms only commit capital to early-stage companies, Alta invests in companies across the continuum — from early-stage company formation to later-stage opportunities. Alta divides its investments into two families of funds, reflecting its commitment to new company formation and funding of established life sciences companies. The ACP funds focus on early-stage opportunities in both the life sciences and information technology industries, while the Alta BioPharma Partners funds are dedicated to later-stage life sciences companies. In both cases, Alta takes a long-term position and, as a value-added investor, actively works with its portfolio company management teams to help build market leading businesses.

Based in San Francisco, Alta capitalizes on its Bay Area locale and proximity to several leading universities that have played significant roles in the emergence of the life sciences industry. Alta currently counts the following local Bay Area companies among its portfolio of investments:

ACLARA Biosciences
AGY Therapeutics
BioMedicines
Corcept Therapeutics
Corgentech
Cytokinetics
DiscoveRx
Dynavax Technologies
Exhale Therapeutics
Genteric
Kosan Biosciences
NeurogesX
Onyx Pharmaceuticals
Plexxikon
Renovis
Rigel Pharmaceuticals
Telik
Vitra Bioscience

Through its considerable industry network, Alta has invested in these existing portfolio companies and cultivated strong relationships with many of the industry's biggest successes, including Genentech, Chiron, Cephalon, Millennium, InterMune and Aviron. Alta leverages these important alliances to further support the scientific and operational objectives of its portfolio companies, providing support in several key areas, including management team development, clinical strategy and operational planning.

With its history of identifying and funding promising life-sciences companies, Alta Partners remains committed to working with exceptional entrepreneurs and providing its portfolio companies with the financing, guidance and extensive network of relationships necessary to build highly successful ventures. ■

Alta Partners
One Embarcadero Center, Ste. 4050
San Francisco, CA 94111
Phone: 415-362-4022
Fax: 415-362-6178
www.altapartners.com

AltaPartners

Amersham Biosciences
Helping to make molecular medicine a reality

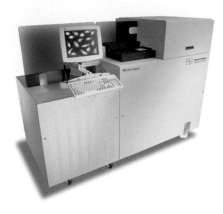

The sequencing of the human genome has quietly left the news, but its promise is still very much in the making. That breakthrough offers a tremendous opportunity to look at the molecular basis of disease, not only to hone the drug discovery process, but also to treat the root causes of disease — one patient at a time.

Getting there, though, requires the right tools. That's what Amersham Biosciences aims to provide.

A leader in the field of life-science instrumentation, Amersham is focusing its extensive research on creating technology to enable the molecular medicine revolution — from optical imagers to the microarrays and sequencers needed to study our genes, cells, tissues and organs - and thereby create a future in which disease will be better understood, diagnosed sooner and treated or prevented more effectively.

"With our Incell Analyzer, for example, we're leveraging our optical imaging skills to enable scientists to look at the impact of a drug candidate on live cells," explains David Weber, president of Amersham's North America Region. "With that technology, scientists will be able to see where a drug is going in a certain part of the cell, so we'll be able to better understand drug actions and drug differences on an individual level."

The vision, he says, is to enable personalized medicine: "That's our mission."

Formed in a 1997 merger of Pharmacia Biotech (Sweden) and Amersham Life Sciences (Britain), Amersham Biosciences' roots reach back more than 100 years. Mergers and acquisitions have given Amersham the critical mass to be a global leader in its field, with a significant intellectual-property portfolio in life sciences and diagnostic imaging, and a tremendous customer base of long-term clients. They also gave it the financial structure and clout to build its future.

Today, Amersham Biosciences is based in Piscataway, NJ, with its optical imaging team in Sunnyvale, Calif. The 4,000-employee division represents nearly half of the $2.5 billion in sales of its UK parent, Amersham Plc. The parent company also includes Amersham Health, the leader in clinical diagnostic and predictive imaging products and services in cardiology, neurology and cancer.

The biosciences segment is itself at the forefront in providing integrated systems and solutions for disease research, drug development and manufacture, including the realms of genomics, proteomics, protein separation and drug screening. With more than 50 years of experience in protein science, Amersham builds integrated, high-throughput systems that accelerate protein analysis and allow several thousand proteins to be studied at once. Its products include the MegaBACE DNA Sequencer, AKTA FPLC and the Typhoon Imager, all standard names in the biomedical field.

"Of all the biopharmaceutical companies with drugs that are currently on the market, almost 100 percent of them used our products in the development of those drugs, and 95 percent of them used our products in manufacturing them," Weber says.

Amersham also serves biopharmaceutical manufacturing companies, providing the products and services to help customers integrate the steps from drug discovery to manufacturing. That makes the whole process more efficient, effective and successful.

Efficiency has never been more important.

At a time when it can cost $800 million to take a drug to market and span 10 years — all with the risk of failure at the FDA approval level — the demand for technology to cut that risk has only intensified.

"The pressure is on today in both biotech and the pharmaceutical industry to bring effective drugs to market more quickly," Weber says. Amersham's products are central in helping determine which drug candidates are feasible and which aren't. "We're helping to ensure that our customers spend their time and money in the right direction." ■

Amersham Biosciences
800 Centennial Ave.
PO Box 1327
Piscataway, NJ 08855-1327
732-457-8000
Fax: 732-457-0557

Sunnyvale Facility
928 East Arques Ave.
Sunnyvale, CA 94085
408-773-1222
Fax: 408-737-3184
www.amersham.com

Applikon Biotechnology
Creating the tools of science

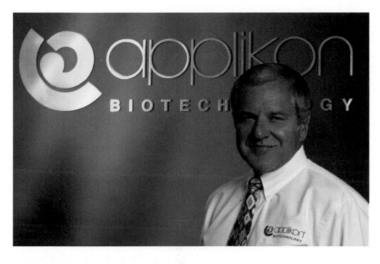

Biotechnology has been marked by headlines of novel approaches and miraculous cures. Yet, behind that fanfare lies another industry as critical to those breakthroughs as the molecular science itself: the instruments and bioreactor systems upon which laboratories depend. Central to that world is Applikon.

The subsidiary of a privately held Dutch company, Applikon Inc. has made a name for itself over the past 20 years in building bioreactors for research laboratories. And as the biotechnology industry has grown from core research into mass production of drugs like Herceptin, Applikon has also expanded to help its customers move into production mode.

At the heart of that growth is a focus on innovation and new development, marked by an ongoing commitment to investing a considerable amount of its income into new product research.

"We've always placed a lot of value on the innovative side of business," says Applikon Inc. president John Chory. "It's been that way since day one, and I don't see that philosophy changing."

Founded in 1973, Applikon's history is one of organic expansion to serve growing industries. The parent company, Applikon Dependable Instruments BV, originally focused on online chemical analyzers to supply petrochemical, food processing, high-technology and environmental companies. In 1983, it opened a US subsidiary in Austin, Texas, to serve the petrochemical industry and supply fermentation equipment to some of the earliest biotech companies, including what was then a small company called Genentech. As biotechnology grew in the late 1980s, Applikon changed its focus to the new industry and moved its US headquarters to Foster City to be closer to the biotech hub.

"Our company was founded on three concepts: quality of products, quality of service and quality of people," Chory says. What put them on the map, though, was their flexibility. Because Applikon has taken a modular approach to its systems, it has been able to readily customize them for each client. "We can change very easily to adjust to the need of the customer, while still maintaining the foundation of our company."

That was especially important in the 1980s, when biotechnology was in its infancy and scientists still weren't sure what equipment they needed. By creating modular systems, Applikon was able to apply scientists' feedback to real solutions. Clearly, that has worked: The company has been profitable since the late 1980s and its sales have tripled in the last five years, while many of its competitors have fallen by the wayside.

Two years ago, Applikon also made a bold move into the large-scale bioreactor segment, becoming the third-largest provider in that arena and enabling it to supply such projects as the Chinese government's large-scale vaccine plants. As a result, Applikon now makes everything from small-scale bioreactors for laboratories to production-scale systems for licensed cGMP facilities.

As a result, Applikon is a world leader in bioreactors and fermentors for laboratories, with systems known for their dependability and ease of use. That segment now represents two-thirds of the parent company's business and is projected to comprise 75 percent by 2008. In the past year alone, it has opened new facilities in Clinton, New Jersey and Foster City; gained its ISO 9001 certification in Europe and begun moving its bioreactor production from the Netherlands to the United States.

With the rising number of FDA approvals in biotechnology, the need for those systems will only increase.

"As long as people can find a way to improve their quality of life through biotechnology," Chory believes, "there will always be a demand in the market for these goods." ∎

Applikon Inc.
1180 Chess Dr.
Foster City, CA 94404
650-578-1396
Fax: 650-578-8836
www.applikon.com

Applied Biosystems

When James Watson and Francis Crick announced in 1953 that they had discovered the "secret of life" (the fundamental structure of DNA), a revolution in the life sciences was born. The discovery marked the beginning of the modern era of genetics and enabled researchers to begin elucidating the underlying mechanisms of disease. Researchers around the world embarked on finding genes, understanding their protein products and unraveling the underlying causes and cures of disease. This launched a genetic "gold rush," and in 1981, Applied Biosystems was founded to provide the "picks and the shovels" to the biotechnology industry.

Established more than 20 years ago, Applied Biosystems has an established history of developing innovative products and services for life science research, pharmaceutical research and development, and forensic and agricultural testing. These technologies have become the cornerstones for modern life science research and catalysts in the life science revolution.

"These tools are essential for researchers to make new discoveries and more effectively and efficiently bring drugs to market," says Michael W. Hunkapiller, PhD, president of

Applied Biosystems, an Applera Corporation business. "In order for Applied Biosystems to remain a leading supplier of systems for life science research, we must be able to anticipate the needs of customers and continue to provide advanced solutions for complex biological problems."

KEY BREAKTHROUGHS, ESSENTIAL PRODUCTS

The following contains a summary of some of the key technologies developed by Applied Biosystems through its history of innovation:

1982 — Applied Biosystems introduces the first protein sequencer and transforms protein research nearly overnight. Previously, sequencing was so difficult that only approximately 200 scientists worldwide could successfully sequence proteins.

1983 — Applied Biosystems introduces the first successful automated DNA synthesizer, making primers and probes readily available to researchers for the first time. Previously, synthetic DNA was made by tedious manual methods.

1984 — Applied Biosystems introduces the first peptide synthesis systems. This enables researchers to study protein structure and how it relates to protein function.

1986 — Automated DNA sequencing sparks the genomic revolution. Applied Biosystems commercializes the first automated DNA sequencer, supplanting the previous manual, radioactive process. The automated sequencer's ability to digitize data accelerated research and set the stage for computerized analysis, genome sequencing, database development and bioinformatics.

1998 — Applied Biosystems introduces the first production scale system for DNA sequencing, the ABI PRISM® 3700 DNA Analyzer. The 3700 DNA analyzer is introduced when the Human Genome Project reached the sequencing phase of its human genome work and when Celera Genomics embarked on its mission to complete the human genome sequence draft in just three years. The 3700 analyzer proves to be the key to accelerating the Human Genome Project and other large-scale genome projects.

Many of Applied Biosystems' tools have become gold-standard technologies for research in the private and public sectors, and the company now enjoys $1.7 billion in annual sales.

Applied Biosystems' technologies have led to many discoveries, and, today, the company offers a number of advanced solutions to make discovery even easier. These include more than 140,000 ready-to-use SNP genotyping assays and nearly 19,000 functionally

Applied Biosystems employee Christine Dinh loads samples onto the new Applied Biosystems 3730xl DNA Analyzer.

validated and ready-to-use gene expression assays through its Assays-on-Demand™ product line.

"In the life sciences, most breakthroughs — from gene discoveries to the development of treatments for genetic diseases — are likely to have involved the use of Applied Biosystems' technology," Hunkapiller explains.

The company offers solutions that span the entire spectrum of life science discovery and development, from basic discovery, to the execution of clinical trials, to quality assurance, quality control and production in such industries as pharmaceutical, biotechnology and clinical diagnostics. Even research to identify "cold case" criminals from forensic evidence relies on Applied Biosystems' technology. And recently, Applied Biosystems' technology has played a central role in helping researchers in the fight against global health concerns such as SARS, anthrax and the West Nile Virus.

SCIENCE OF INNOVATION

Applied Biosystems has led the industry with its continued commitment to investment in research and development of new products. As biology and related fields of study are converging and traditional laboratory research is complemented with information-based science, Applied Biosystems has expanded its focus to enable researchers to perform "Integrated Science." The convergence of disciplines and the availability of a host of new tools to enable a systems approach to biology will impact life sciences discovery by enabling scientists to study complex interactions between many levels of biological data and processes.

"As our understanding of the human and other genomes has grown, we have begun to realize just how complex the biology of an organism is," Hunkapiller says. "Our job is to be able to serve the biology research world, and you can not do that unless you continually provide them with fresh tools. Life sciences research is constantly challenging us with new problems."

Applied Biosystems has made its mark by understanding the problems that the research world is trying to solve. The top-level research team then works to find tools that will be required and sets about developing those tools.

"If we want to lead the process, you have to know first hand what the problems are and get them manufactured, marketed and supported in researcher's labs," Hunkapiller describes. "Success is not just marketing. It is built on understanding the research community and having your organization focused and devoted to that particular problem."

RECENT ACHIEVEMENTS

• March 2, 2003 — FORTUNE magazine names Applera Corporation as one of *America's Most Admired Companies* under the Medical Products and Equipment category.

• In 2002, Celera Diagnostics, a fifty-fifty joint venture between Applied Biosystems and Celera Genomics, received the *Scientific American 50 Award* for its work in the area of medical diagnostics. The award is the first annual celebration of

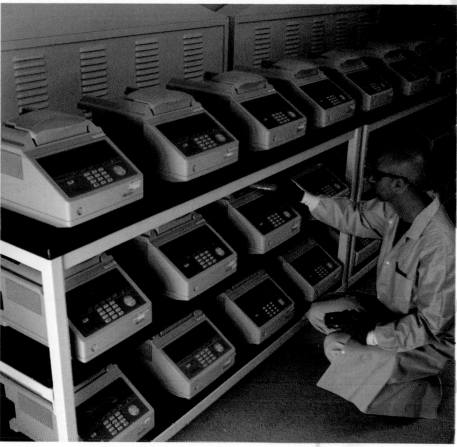

Dave Merrill of Applied Biosystems loads a sample plate on an Applied Biosystems GeneAmp® PCR 9700 System.

visionaries from the worlds of research, industry and politics whose recent accomplishments point toward a brighter technological future for everyone. Celera Diagnostics is located in Alameda, Calif.

• A new expansion facility in Pleasanton, Calif., opened in July 2003.

• Mike Hunkapiller received the first annual *Takeda Award for Techno-Entrepreneurial Achievement for Individual/Humanity Well-Being* for his contribution to the development of automated high-throughput DNA sequencers and the promotion of the foundation of Celera Genomics.

• Applied Biosystems received the *Design News Magazine Quality Award* for the ABI PRISM 3700 DNA Analyzer, which is a production scale sequencer that was employed by both public and private labs to rapidly sequence the human genome.

With offices located throughout the world, including the United Kingdom, France, Germany, Australia, Japan, South America and Foster City, Calif., Applied Biosystems employs more than 4,500 employees. ■

Applied Biosystems
850 Lincoln Centre Drive
Foster City, CA 94404
www.appliedbiosystems.com

Aradigm Corporation

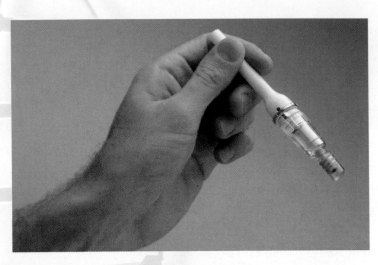

In the biotechnology community today, almost every drug in development is delivered through injection. "What we do at Aradigm is eliminate the use of needles," says Richard Thompson, Chairman and CEO of Aradigm Corporation. Aradigm's proprietary AERx® and Intraject® technologies introduce convenience into the drug delivery experience, without sacrificing the precision of injectable therapy. Both AERx® and Intraject® offer access to systemic circulation through novel delivery mechanisms: The AERx® system delivers molecules to and through the lungs, while the Intraject® system delivers drugs through the skin to the subcutaneous space.

These needle-free, portable drug-delivery systems will greatly improve the lives of many people with disabling disorders. "Diabetes is the leading cause of blindness in the United States," Thompson explains. "It contributes to heart disease, kidney disease and complications that can lead to the amputation of limbs. Because the prescribed therapeutic regimen for diabetes requires people to daily inject themselves with insulin as often as four times a day, resistance to using needles increases the risk of long-term complications."

Aradigm's AERx® system is in Phase 3 clinical trials for the pulmonary delivery of insulin to patients with diabetes and has progressed through Phase 2 trials in its application for acute pain management. The AERx® technology is also being applied to treat life-threatening pulmonary disorders.

"There are many technological advances in the delivery of drugs to treat lung disease," Thompson says, "but the AERx® platform brings a level of efficiency and reproducibility to the process that is far beyond any other inhaler technology to date. With AERx®, drug therapies can become more effective because the drug can be placed in the lung exactly where it needs to go."

Another technology in the advanced stages of development is Intraject®, Aradigm's pen-sized needle-free injection system that comfortably delivers liquid formulations through the skin.

Intraject® is being used as an alternative to conventional pre-filled syringes to deliver small molecules such as those in triptan therapy for migraines, PEGylated proteins for hepatitis C and monoclonal antibodies for a variety of applications.

"Both platforms are very easy for people of all ages to use," Thompson says. "Our AERx® devices control patient inhalation and deliver the drug at the right time in the breath. With Intraject®, patients simply place the unit against the skin to administer the drug."

Aradigm's collaborations with global pharmaceutical companies are increasing awareness of needle-free options and how therapies become more cost-effective by avoiding needle-stick injuries, while also allowing for home administration instead of costly office visits.

"Our goal is to have true partnerships working collaboratively to develop important products. Novo Nordisk, Roche, GlaxoSmithKline and Abbott Laboratories bring to our collaborations expertise about the marketplace and customers, as well as the molecules. This is possible because these companies are already leaders in the therapeutic areas in which we work," Thompson explains. "What Aradigm brings to the partnerships is the know-how to formulate and deliver drugs in ways that are optimized for the particular product category and patient population."

Much of Aradigm's know-how comes from the experience and talent of the employees at its Hayward headquarters. "We draw many of our employees from the very well-trained populations on both the east and west sides of the Bay," Thompson says. "The advantage of being in Hayward is that the real-estate prices are lower, yet we are still very central." ■

Aradigm Corporation
3929 Point Eden Way
Hayward, CA 94545
510-265-9000
Fax: 510-265-0277
www.aradigm.com

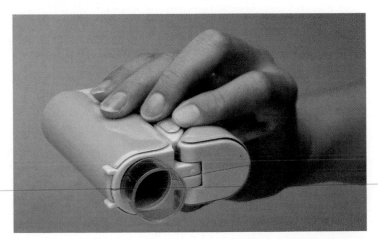

Arriva Pharmaceuticals, Inc.

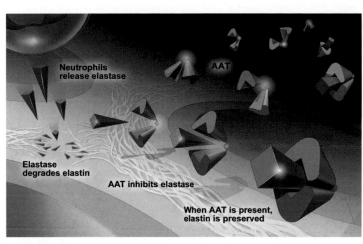

During periods of inflammation, immune system cells such as the neutrophil secrete proteases that, when uncontrolled, can degrade the elastic fibers of the lung. Arriva's nebulized rAAT intercepts the proteases before they can cause lung damage.

The focus Arriva Pharmaceuticals, a biotechnology company, is not only to conduct laboratory research but develop medicines. "The science in the company is focused on the development of products for defined areas of clinical need, such as heredity emphysema" says Martin Preuveneers, PhD, Chairman and CEO at Arriva.

Arriva creates inhibitors of proteases, the enzymes used to degrade proteins. These inhibitors have therapeutic applications for respiratory diseases such as emphysema and asthma, as well as for dermatological conditions such as dermatitis and psoriasis. The Alameda Company uses proprietary science to turn a biosynthetic form of the protease inhibitor alpha 1-antitrypsin (AAT) into medicine.

With an eye toward the market, Arriva has capitalized on a very specialized sector in the life sciences. "There are only a certain number of proteins that have human health-care applications," Dr. Preuveneers explains, "and there are not too many of these naturally occurring proteins left for exploitation. Recombinant AAT represents one of these commercial opportunities."

With 24 employees, Arriva maintains a highly skilled group — two MDs and seven PhDs — who work closely with its corporate partners. Presently, Arriva partners with Baxter Healthcare's BioScience Unit to develop genetically-engineered AAT to treat hereditary emphysema. Arriva has also collaborated with ProMetic Life Sciences to expand the treatment options available for dermatological and other indications.

None of this work would be possible, of course, without the backing of enthusiastic investors. "Having a venture capitalist group, a major insurance company and a prominent bank among our stockholders provides excellent support for our company," Dr. Preuveneers says. In addition to AIG Global Investments and CIBC Capital Partners, MPM Capital — the largest venture fund in health care — has contributed to the $28 million Arriva gathered in 2002 to initiate its clinical trials.

"We are conducting clinical trials with patients suffering from hereditary emphysema and are delivering AAT to the lungs via a nebulizer," Dr. Preuveneers explains. Arriva aims to help physicians respond to a range of respiratory problems by providing a more patient-friendly delivery route. Instead of IV treatment using limited supplies of the plasma-derived AAT, Arriva's approach allows for the unlimited supply of AAT for delivery by inhalation. The blood product is in short supply, and has been recalled on safety grounds on a number of occasions.

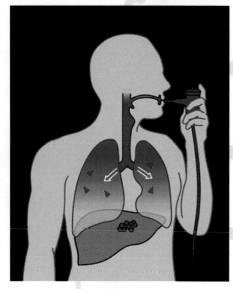

In the individual suffering from hereditary emphysema, release of natural AAT (blue circles) from the liver is blocked. The Arriva solution is to deliver adequate levels of recombinant AAT as a replacement therapy, by nebulization directly into the lung.

Extending the use of recombinant AAT to dermatological conditions, Arriva has also developed topical formations of AAT. "We have also begun trials of a gel that is applied to the skin of patients suffering from atopic dermatitis," Dr. Preuveneers adds.

Arriva is now addressing the unmet need for a drug to treat a form of emphysema: Chronic Obstructive Pulmonary Disease (COPD), a disease caused primarily by cigarette smoking. ∎

Arriva Pharmaceuticals, Inc.
2020 Challenger Dr.
Alameda, CA 94501
510-337-1250
Fax: 510-337-1251
www.arrivapharm.com

The Avicena Group Inc.
Regulating Cellular Energy

Avicena VP of Operations Belinda Tsao-Nivaggioli, Ph.D., believes the Bay Area offers the ideal location for strategic partnership and talented personnel.

The Avicena Group Inc. is an emerging biotechnology company whose core scientific platform is based on the regulation of cellular energy. Founded as a research laboratory in 1994, Avicena's pioneering science builds on the finding that cellular energy defects are common to many diseases, including major neuro-degenerative diseases such as Alzheimer's, Parkinson's, Huntington's and Amyotrophic Lateral Sclerosis (ALS), also known as Lou Gehrig's Disease.

"We don't consider ourselves to be a pharmaceutical company. We do the science, we patent our work and then we out-license the applications," explains Belinda Tsao Nivaggioli, PhD, vice president of operations at Avicena. "We are a small company focused on developing useful applications from our core science, and to do this we work with a strong network of university and medical care-based researchers and clinicians."

Avicena's core science is based on the activities of the Creatine Kinase/PhosphoCreatine system, which provides energy transport and buffering in tissues with intermittently high and fluctuating energy demands, including the brain, retina, heart and skeletal muscles. Creatine kinase is also a critical component in making adenosine triphosphate (ATP), the basic energy source for all cells. Other substrates of the creatine kinase system modulate cellular energy, prolong cellular life and protect against cell death. Avicena's laboratory work has shown that creatine compounds are beneficial across a range of neuro-degenerative diseases, various types of brain cells and locations in the brain.

Avicena applies that core science to both pharmaceutical and over-the-counter (OTC) drugs. The company is developing pharmaceutical products in five therapeutic classes: neurological disease, oncology, dermatology, ophthalmology and endocrinology. In the OTC area, Avicena focuses on cosmaceuticals, medical foods and dietary supplements.

The company now owns several trademarks and has more than 25 patents (published & pending), all of which address the modulation of cellular energy to mitigate the disease process, either by increasing energy to extend cell life, as in neurology, or by decreasing energy to precipitate apoptosis, or programmed cell death, as in oncology.

In February 2002, Avicena received its first Orphan Drug designation from the US Food and Drug Administration, for the use of creatine in the treatment of ALS. The company is also developing an orphan drug candidate for Huntington's Disease.

Avicena has ongoing clinical trials in more than 30 institutions on a range of neuro-degenerative disease applications, many of which are likely Orphan Drug candidates. The company also recently received Investigative New Drug (IND) approval from the FDA for Phase II clinical studies on the effect of cyclocreatine in combination with other anti-cancer therapies, for which it is actively seeking development partners. Cyclocreatine is a creatine kinase substrate that lowers the energetic processes of cancer cells to normal levels, making them more susceptible to other cancer therapies and more likely to undergo programmed cell death.

The company's over-the-counter products include NEOtine™, a creatine dietary supplement for those with neurodegenerative diseases, which is sold through the company's website. It also has launched five anti-aging creatine products in conjunction with a prestigious global skincare company.

Avicena's founders — Rima Kaddurah-Daouk, Paul Schimmel, Julius Rebek Jr. and M. Flint Beal — are respected researchers from Dana Farber Cancer Institute, Scripps Research Institute and Cornell Medical School. The company views its strong ties with leading scientists, clinicians and patient advocacy organizations as one of its core competencies. As a result, Avicena's base in Palo Alto is a vital component of its growth strategy.

"We will be expanding and we need to be close to first-rate research institutes and universities," Tsao Nivaggioli explains. 'The Bay Area offers us both a great talent pool and a long list of ideal partnership candidates." ■

The Avicena Group Inc.
Business Office:
288 Hamilton Ave., 3rd Flr.
Palo Alto, CA 94301
415-397-2880
Fax: 415-397-2898

Research and Development:
One Cambridge Center, 5th Flr.
Cambridge, MA 02142
617-225-0501
Fax: 627-225-0502
www.avicenagroup.com

BayBio
(Bay Area Bioscience Center)
Bridge to the Bioscience Community

The San Francisco Bay Area is a unique and diverse place that leads the world in medical innovation, research and the development of life-saving therapies. Blessed with cutting-edge research institutions and an ever-growing group of eager start-ups, the region is home to the oldest and largest biotechnology cluster in the world.

At the forefront of the biotech region in the Bay Area, "BayBio is the voice of the world's largest bioscience cluster, bringing the community together into one collective group, promoting its science and innovation, and providing a forum for members to exchange information," says Caitlyn Waller, president of BayBio. As the brainchild of some of the biggest names in biotechnology, along with high-profile civic and economic planners, BayBio was formed in 1990. All involved were convinced of the potential of biotechnology as an economic engine for the region, hence Bay-Bio's willingness to inform, facilitate and foster growth by bringing together the media, local governments, the general public and the bioscience community. Serving as the voice of bioscience, BayBio effectively helps to ensure biotech's mission stays at the top of elected officials' agendas. BayBio works to ensure that the region remains the #1 location for cutting-edge biotech businesses by facilitating a cohesive working environment that ensures the competitiveness of the Bay Area.

Biotech companies are hard at work on medicine's promise in the Bay Area. Together, they employ more than 85,000 people, generating $2.7 billion in exports. The Bay Area is seen as a model for other clusters, having grown from an idea into an important pillar in Northern California's economy, in just 27 years.

"Biotech is crucial to the California economy," Waller says, "and in order to maintain our competitiveness, state and local government must understand the research and development, manufacturing and infrastructure needs of the industry."

BayBio and the Life Sciences Strategic Action Plan Partners have created a ten-year plan for the life sciences industry in Northern California. "Taking Action for Tomorrow: Bay Area Life Sciences Strategic Action Plan" provides short and long-term recommendations to maintain our cluster's competitiveness. BayBio Director of Government Relations Sue Markland Day serves as an educator for both legislators and industry executives by helping companies understand what legislative changes could affect the already highly regulated industry. The organization has helped to shape public policy on the issues of stem cells, cloning, and also rallied against a legislative initiative that would have hampered research on species of fish by restricting transport.

BayBio has worked with local legislators like San Francisco Supervisor Sophie Maxwell to help provide information for people to learn about the distinct needs of the industry. Day also played a role in the investigation of East Bay clusters for a regional study. Other issues on the BayBio agenda include access to capital, manufacturing, and transportation in the Bay Area. BayBio has successfully induced the Bay Area Water Transportation Authority to evaluate the viability of ferry service from the East Bay to South San Francisco.

Members of this nonprofit organization are welcomed into a collective group, and show their support of and enhancing Northern California's bioscience image. To its members, BayBio provides informational and mentoring seminars, timely briefings on regulatory and legal issues, legislative working groups with an emphasis on access to capital, a monthly e-magazine, discounts on BayBio-sponsored events, bioscience and service company directories, free-postings on its website, referrals to the press, receptions, and a discount purchasing program (under development).

In 2001 BayBio began a new bioentrepreneurial forum, Bay-BioNEST (Network for Entrepreneurial Strategies and Tactics), which showcases BayBio's commitment to advancing and strengthening the industry. This new outlet assists in the formation of new biotechnology companies by linking company builders and entrepreneurs at many levels.

Filling a need for advocacy, education of the community, and influence on public policy, BayBio works to ensure that the Bay Area will remain the center of biotechnology for years to come. BayBio welcomes new members, from the bioscience and service industry sectors. ■

BayBio
651 Gateway Blvd., Ste. 1145
South San Francisco, CA 94080
650-871-7101
Fax: 650-871-7555
info@baybio.org
www.baybio.org

Bayer HealthCare LLP

Bayer HealthCare is part of the Germany-based Bayer Group, an international provider of health care and chemicals products worldwide.

Best known for its flagship product, *Bayer Aspirin*, Bayer produces a broad range of health care, crop protection, polymer and chemical products that help diagnose and treat diseases, purify water, preserve local landmarks, protect crops, and advance automobile safety and durability. Bayer HealthCare is dedicated to improving patients' quality of life by providing quality health care products in the pharmaceutical, biological products, animal health, consumer care and diagnostics areas.

The Bayer campus in Berkeley houses three elements of the global Bayer HealthCare organization. The first, Bayer Biotechnology, focuses on the research and development of medicines for diseases such as cancer, HIV, and diabetes. Bayer Biological Products, the second Berkeley component, is responsible for manufacturing Kogenate® FS, a treatment for Hemophilia A, as well as other plasma-derived biological pharmaceuticals. The nucleic acid testing unit of Bayer's clinical Diagnostics Group rounds out the campus and provides DNA analysis tests for HIV and Hepatitis, including the FDA-approved VERSANT® HIV bDNA assay used for direct quantification of HIV-1 RNA in the plasma of people living with HIV.

"We have unique expertise in developing the extremely complicated and precise processes used in protein expression," says Robert Kuhn, Vice President of Process Sciences in Biotechnology. "Our research and development team can take experimental compounds from the early discovery phase into commercial production, so new medicines can quickly reach the patients they are designed to help."

The Bayer HealthCare location in Berkeley celebrated its 100-year anniversary in 2003. During the past century, the campus has grown and redirected its focus a number of times

to respond to the public's need for health care products. It is now a world-class research and biologicals manufacturing facility. Founded as Cutter Laboratories in 1903, the Berkeley site became a member of the Bayer family in 1974. Bayer's Berkeley campus continues to expand. A new Diagnostics Group building was recently dedicated, while new manufacturing facilities are currently under construction.

Bayer's employee community is dedicated to serving the needs of patients worldwide. The Berkeley site is committed to providing a diverse workplace that supports the professional growth of its employees. Dr. Ellen Cheung, Director of the department of Preclinical Development says, "Being part of Bayer in Berkeley is most satisfying because we produce unique, life-saving medicine while working in an environment that really values employees' achievements and contributions."

Bayer Berkeley has an employee community of 1700 people specializing in biologicals manufacturing research and development, production technology, marketing and business development, and a broad range of other disciplines. Bayer is committed to actively supporting programs that benefit patients, and the Berkeley community at large, through the Bayer Foundation and its active employee volunteer and community outreach programs that assist many Bay Area non-profit organizations and public schools. ■

Bayer HealthCare LLP
800 Dwight Way
Berkeley, CA 94710
510-705-5000
Fax: 510-705-7878
www.bayer.com

BioMarin

Matching proven science with proven needs

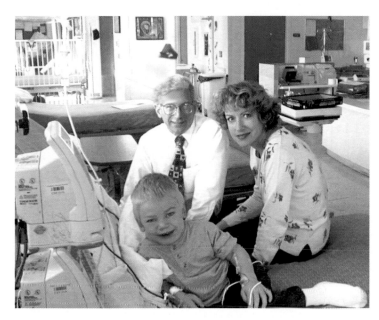

Not many biotech companies have taken a drug to market just six years from startup. Still fewer do so with an additional drug close behind in their pipeline. But at BioMarin Pharmaceutical Inc., the strategy has always been a little different.

Founded in 1997, the Novato-based company focuses on developing and commercializing enzyme therapies for serious, life-threatening diseases and conditions, with highly targeted patient populations. The first of those drugs has its roots in the research of Emil Kakkis, MD, PhD, formerly at the University of California, Los Angeles and now senior vice president of business operations for BioMarin. A pediatrician by training, Dr. Kakkis' team developed Aldurazyme®, a recombinant form of the enzyme alpha-L-iduronidase, which is deficient in children with a debilitating genetic disorder called MPS I. What Dr. Kakkis needed was a company to develop his enzyme treatment into a consistent therapy for widespread use.

Six years later, that 290-person company has secured FDA and EMEA approval for Aldurazyme, and the product is being marketed by Genzyme. Aldurazyme's approval represents a critical milestone for BioMarin, a "transforming event" in the words of Fredric Price, BioMarin's chairman and CEO.

It also represents a validation for BioMarin's strategy. The company does not do classical biotech discovery research;

instead, it looks for known enzymes involved in life-threatening diseases for which the company can be first or foremost in the market.

In 2003, BioMarin completed two financings for more than $211 million. These funds are targeted toward BioMarin's pipeline, which includes another enzyme replacement therapy, Aryplase™, for the treatment of patients with the genetic disease MPS VI, which is in a pivotal Phase 3 clinical trial. In addition, BioMarin is developing Vibrilase™, a topically applied enzyme therapy for the treatment of severe burns, which is in a Phase 1b clinical trial. The company is also evaluating numerous preclinical-stage product candidates, including a potential treatment for patients with PKU (phenylketonuria), a genetic disorder affecting approximately 50,000 patients in the United States and Europe, as well as NeuroTrans™, a technology being evaluated as a method to deliver both enzymes and other therapeutic molecules to the brain via traditional intravenous infusion.

"Within six years, BioMarin has proven its ability to execute the company strategy of selecting product candidates for diseases and conditions that have well-understood biology, that represent a clear, unmet medical need and promise a clear-cut clinical development profile," Price says. "Now, with an approved product on the market, we are in an even stronger position to leverage our core competencies in the area of drug development and manufacturing, and will continue to build business and stockholder value." ∎

BioMarin Pharmaceutical Inc.
371 Bel Marin Keys Blvd., Ste. 210
Novato, CA 94949
415-506-6700
Fax: 415-382-7889
www.BMRN.com

Matching Proven Science With Proven Needs.

Replace the enzyme, help control the disease.

bioKinetics

As an engineering, design, and project management company for the biotechnology and biopharmaceutical industries, bioKinetics is unmatched in the services and products it delivers. This privately held business opened its doors in 1996 to solve the problems of these rapidly growing industries, where consulting and building expertise continue to be in high demand.

From its offices in Emeryville, bioKinetics delivers engineering capabilities to benefit life sciences companies in the Bay Area and beyond. "Our work in bioprocessing engineering is specific to the manufacturing of drugs," says Leo Krieg, director of business development at bioKinetics' Philadelphia headquarters. "Our engineering goes from conceptual designs of manufacturing operations to construction and validation of those facilities," he adds. "We work within the necessary constraints of the FDA regulations and the current good manufacturing processes (cGMP) to improve the cost-effectiveness and productivity of manufacturing facilities."

"In Emeryville, we've built up a core competency in bioprocessing design and facility delivery by means of design-build methodology," says Sue Cost, bioKinetics business development manager in the Western region. "That's just a way of getting the job done faster with a high level of accountability to our customers."

For pharmaceutical companies with products in late phase II clinical trials, the next step in the drug development process is often toward manufacturing. At that stage, the decision becomes whether to outsource production or undertake the manufacturing process internally. "For companies just starting out," says Krieg, a chemical engineer who worked with design

firm Life Sciences International for about 10 years before joining bioKinetics, "the next question may be: to build or to buy? When an enterprise chooses to build, that's where we come in. We help companies conceptualize their facilities. We work with scientists and engineers to get an understanding of the processes and scale that will be required."

Between 1998 and 2000, bioKinetics acquired several businesses that allowed the company to expand beyond its original design and engineering capacities. These businesses became the basis for the company's equipment design and manufacturing division. At the bioKinetics center in Toronto, designers work on specific bioprocess and critical utilities systems, such as cell culture bioreactors, microbial fermenters, clean-in-place systems, waste inactivation systems and purification modules, helping to make bioKinetics among the leaders in bioprocess technology.

bioKinetics also takes great pride in its simulation and modeling services. Total Optimization Plant Simulation (K-TOPS™) is the company's proprietary tool that creates multiple design scenarios to model factors such as capacity and impact on critical resources. "We're currently using our simulation services to eliminate production bottlenecks at Amgen and Chiron," Krieg says. bio-Kinetics also relies on K-TOPS™ during the design phase when simulation and modeling can help drive overall facility costs down. "We have saved our customers literally millions of dollars in capital expenditure without compromising their capacity and throughput," he adds.

Kinetics Modular Systems, the equipment division of bioKinetics, manufactures the stainless steel tanks and piping systems that provide the clean environments necessary to drug manufacturers. "When you walk through a biotech facility, it's like a cross between a hospital operating room and a chemical plant," Krieg says. bioKinetics custom designs and develops

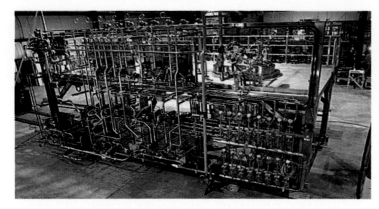

modular equipment that ensures the sanitary and environmentally safe working operations required by the biopharmaceutical community.

In a joint venture with one of the leading raw materials suppliers to the biotech industry, bioKinetics has formed HyNetics®, a company devoted to single-use process systems. Through this partnership, bioKinetics continues to extend its offerings in ways that improve both the quality of products and the cost-effectiveness of solutions. "The focus of the collaboration," Krieg explains, "is to introduce to the marketplace a way to help companies more easily meet their cleaning requirements. Through single-use systems, cleaning risks are totally eliminated."

In the Bay Area, bioKinetics has partnered with biotech and biopharmaceutical companies such as BioMarin, Berlex, Chiron and Bayer, and also enjoys successes with new businesses. "BioMarin Pharmaceutical was a start-up when we began working together," Cost explains, "and we're on our fourth project with them now." Another client bioKinetics works with in California is IDEC Pharmaceuticals, a company that recently merged with Biogen.

Through the network of businesses bioKinetics has nurtured, the company gathers all of the materials and resources it needs to provide all-in-one solutions for biotechnology manufacturers. "We partner with those who are familiar with local codes and regulations and can deliver the final detail design of the building," Cost says. "We facilitate installation and construction of the facilities and ultimately the validation through internal and external resources."

"We dedicate ourselves to helping the industry find better ways to get products to market," he adds. "We optimize whatever parameters are of interest to the customers, limited budget and speed-to-market being two of the most common." ■

bioKinetics
1335 Stanford Ave., Ste. 400
Emeryville, CA 94608
510-594-3000
Fax: 510-595-0220
www.kineticsbiopharm.com   Engineering Services
www.ktops.com   Simulation and Modeling Services
www.hynetics.com   Single-Use Process Solutions
www.kineticsmodular.com   Equipment Services

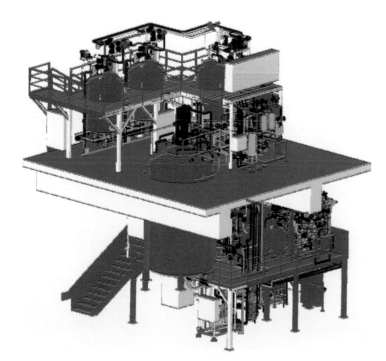

bioKinetics
Optimum Process Solutions-Concept to Product

BioPathology Sciences Inc.

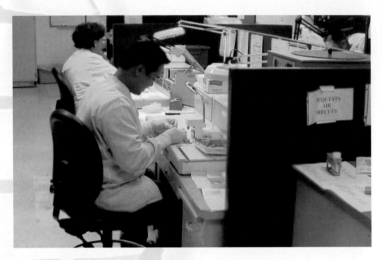

practices, because of both the cutting-edge science on which their technology is based and because of the company's commitment to excellence.

"BioPathology offers an array of special stains to help delineate specific cell types and determine what effect a given treatment might have had on particular target tissues or cells," Dr. Katzen says. "We even have the expertise to take on large panels of new antibodies and evaluate their staining characteristics in a high-throughput manner. Just as importantly," she adds, "we respect and protect the confidentiality of our clients and their intellectual property."

Biotechnology companies know when they contact Biopathology Sciences, they gain access to the best and the most affordable expertise. "Hiring us on an as-needed basis," Dr. Katzen says, "is much more cost-effective than keeping pathologists and trained technicians on staff or purchasing expensive equipment necessary to do the work in-house. We have automation and economies of scale to allow us to work for companies on a contractual basis, just when they need us."

BioPathology Sciences combines scientific expertise with a diagnostic consultative service and an exceptional technical infrastructure to stay ahead of the competition. "We're comfortable discussing both molecular biology and morphology," Dr. Katzen adds. "I don't know of anybody else who can do this." ■

BioPathology Sciences Medical Corporation
393 E. Grand Avenue, Ste. I
South San Francisco, CA 94080
650-616-2950
Fax: 650-737-8920
www.biopathology.net

BioPathology Sciences in South San Francisco provides expert support in histology and pathology to biopharmaceutical companies, medical device businesses and academic researchers. "We process tissues so that they can be examined under the microscope and we evaluate tissues in order to diagnose and interpret abnormalities or determine patterns of reactivity," says Carolyn Katzen, MD, director of BioPathology Sciences. "We help businesses take their products to market by explaining the effects that their drugs, devices and procedures have on human and animal tissue samples."

Three years ago, nine board-certified medical pathologists banded together to form BioPathology Sciences. "At first," Dr. Katzen explains, "the company provided services only for the patient-related medical work we do as pathologists because we were unable to find a satisfactory alternative. Once we set up the lab, we found that our knowledge and expertise was in high demand with the biotech companies in the area."

After completing residency training in pathology at UCSF and a fellowship in surgical pathology at Stanford, Dr. Katzen began practice as a pathologist at local hospitals and clinics. With so much Bay Area experience, Dr. Katzen and BioPathology have found themselves perfectly situated among the neighboring biotechnology communities. The relationships they have developed from these networks have greatly contributed to their successes.

"Our location in South San Francisco's industrial corridor makes it easy for company scientists and others to drop by and look at samples under the microscope by our side," Katzen adds. "We have personal relationships with each company, and people like the fact that we provide very individualized service."

Those personal relationships flourish in part because there's more than just a smile behind the excellent service at Biopathology. Pathologists at the company can deliver solutions that meet the FDA's cGLP, or current good laboratory

BioQuest Incorporated

"I moved into executive recruitment because of my desire to put together successful teams," says Jürgen Weber, PhD, MBA, and managing partner at BioQuest Incorporated. "When I was managing scientists myself, I found it was extremely important for the success of the project to bring together the right people," he adds.

"Capital and advanced technologies are often cited as the most valuable resources in the biotech industry, but successful enterprises are made through people," Dr. Weber explains. "All companies must form the right teams to translate money and technologies into commercial success."

In 1985, after years of work in direct research and in industry, Dr. Weber and Roger Anderson founded BioQuest and helped form such teams for venture-backed companies in the life sciences and medical-device industries. As one of the premier boutique firms to identify and attract executive-level talent for the health-care industry, BioQuest includes among its clients many local companies such as Telik Inc., in addition to well-known West Coast venture capital firms such as Bay City Capital, Versant Ventures, Frazier & Co. and Alloy Ventures.

"Being in the San Francisco area means we are in the hotbed of biotechnology where business acumen and innovative technologies come together to form new companies," Dr. Weber adds. "We are connected to many of the key players in the nation, but our searches do not stop with the United States. We look for talent worldwide, from Australia to Asia and Europe."

BioQuest consultants work closely with clients throughout the search process to identify and secure the required executive leadership, whether that is in the form of a CEO or president, a board member or director. "Our methods are complex and range from the analytical to the intuitive," Dr. Weber explains. "We know what makes people successful, especially in an entrepreneurial setting." Also built into BioQuest's careful selection process is a validation of findings. "Our network of reliable sources confirms for us that information we have gathered from direct interviewing of the candidates is correct," he adds.

Many times the perfect person for the job may not be the candidate who appears most qualified on paper. "Another important aspect of our work is determining how an executive fits into a current team," Dr. Weber says. "Part of what we are paid for is team building, making sure that various characters and temperaments will work synergistically together for the benefit of the company."

BioQuest offers its very personalized service in four areas of practice: Pharmaceuticals/Biotechnology, Medical Devices, Healthcare Services and Healthcare Information Technology. Already well established in the first three markets, BioQuest is branching out into the growing market of Healthcare IT, a specialty at the intersection of health-care services and information technology. Advances in this field will allow for more efficient and error-reduced communications between health-care providers, insurance companies, patients and patient educators. BioQuest sees a significant need for executives in this field who will adapt these new tools to the marketplace.

With three PhD-level professionals on staff, BioQuest is unmatched in the technical expertise it offers. "One of the advantages of working with BioQuest is that our technical understanding is at the highest level," Dr. Weber says. "Unlike most other search firms, we bridge technology and science with the business interests of our clients."

Dr. Weber describes perhaps the best way BioQuest stands apart from competitors when he says: "We directly use our own technical and market knowledge to evaluate people. Our greatest strength is our depth of knowledge and our many years of expertise in matching people with business opportunities." ∎

BioQuest Incorporated
100 Spear Street, Ste. 1125
San Francisco, CA 94105
415-777-2422
Fax: 415-777-4363
www.bioquestinc.com

Brayer Electric Co.

Serving the Bay Area in industry and science for Over 75 Years

Old photographs of San Francisco show gas lamps on the corners, dimly lighting the streets. To George F. Brayer, those shadows spelled opportunity.

In 1928, George F. Brayer created a company with the goal of bringing the latest technology — electrical power — to San Francisco. Brayer Electric took hold in the earliest stage of the snowballing demand for electricity, gradually growing throughout the Depression. Then came the mid-1940s, with the post-World War II expansion and Public Works projects. Relying on his company's decade of experience, Brayer opportunely positioned the business for the impending construction boom.

Today, Brayer Electric Co. is celebrating not only 75 years of illuminating the Bay Area, but also its third generation of Brayer leadership. Throughout the years, the company has distinguished itself in both the quality of its work and its ability to serve cutting-edge projects and industries. Among those are the "Path of Gold" lighting on Market Street, the Stanford Linear Accelerator Center, the Lawrence Berkeley Laboratories, Moscone Center, Candlestick Park and numerous San Francisco high rises: the Hyatt Regency, Hibernia Bank and Hilton Towers, among others.

"Our success is based on the core values that my father established in the early 20th century," says Ted Brayer, who became president in 1978 and is now in the process of passing the reins to his son, George F. Brayer II. "He was a visionary with the ability to see the future of public works projects and at the same time to focus on the very immediate present. He understood that as a leader in the industry, he had to emphasize workmanship, field management and fiscal integrity. Those values have created who we are today."

As a result, the firm is now one of the most respected electrical contracting companies in the West, with hundreds of projects under its belt. From the small shop his father created, Ted grew the company organically and by acquisition to more than 150 electricians, making it one of Northern California's largest electrical contractors.

Just as his father followed the trends in large government projects like the NASA Wind Tunnel and the Camp Parks projects in the '30s and '40s, Ted has also adjusted the company to meet the Bay Area's needs. While maintaining the company's industrial work, he followed the growth in high rises from the 1960s into the '80s, then the technology boom into

the 1990s. Unlike many contractors in the late 1990s Brayer made a decision to scale back.

"During the boom of the late 1990s, we realized that most contractors were starting to get over-extended," George explains. Brayer decided not to follow this path of rapid growth, but rather maintain a volume that fits into core values. "This decision allowed us to keep our high standard of quality, and maintain good relationships with our customers and general contractors. We did not have to rely on project managers and electricians who were not capable of managing and installing according to Brayer's standards. Furthermore, it was clear to us that the pace at which the construction industry was expanding was clearly not sustainable," says George. This approach has given Brayer the opportunity to grow at a more manageable pace, and acquire competitors who fit into their model. "Now we are actually growing while others are still looking for ways to cut cost."

Today, the company is focusing on its key customer's renewed construction needs, while leveraging 75 years of expertise in building cutting-edge science centers to serve the Bay Area's growing biotechnology industry. Among its projects are the Prusiner Laboratory at UCSF and laboratories at UC Berkeley, where Brayer installed the power and controls for both labs and clean rooms.

Its core values, however, remain the same: hard work and dedication to quality.

"We've always been driven by the desire to outperform the competition and exceed our clients' expectations," George says. "Whether it's an industrial construction project or a service call at the local grocery store, we're here for our customers. That's how we started, and that's how we'll keep growing into the next century." ∎

Brayer Electric Co.
Main Office
15095 Wicks Blvd.
San Leandro, CA 94577
510-346-7012
Fax: 510-346-0718
www.brayerelectric.com

Catellus Development Corporation

Mission Bay: the new home for biotechnology in San Francisco

On the southern end of San Francisco's historic water-front lies one of biotechnology's newest prospects and is among one of the most exciting mixed-use urban developments in the world: Mission Bay, a 303-acre project. The heart of the Mission Bay project is UCSF's new Research Campus and the Life Sciences Campus for private industry. The project is the result of a collective vision between the city of San Francisco, UCSF and Catellus Development Corporation, master developer of the project, to create one of the most innovative and rewarding public-private environments ever built for the life-sciences industry.

San Francisco's newest neighborhood is well underway with several parks, offices and nearly 1,000 apartment and condominium homes in various stages of completion, and more are in the planning stages. Retail establishments including Starbucks, Safeway and Borders are moving to the project to serve the neighborhood, with many more in the plans.

UCSF AT MISSION BAY

UCSF's 43-acre Mission Bay Research Campus will ultimately support up to 9,000 scientists, researchers, graduates and administrators, and house more than 48 major research laboratories in 20 structures. Nearly one million square feet is under construction, with the first building, Genentech Hall, already being occupied. Next-door is Mission Bay's Life Sciences Campus, which is designed to give companies ready access to one of the nation's leading research universities — an institution committed to collaboration and technology transfer with private industry.

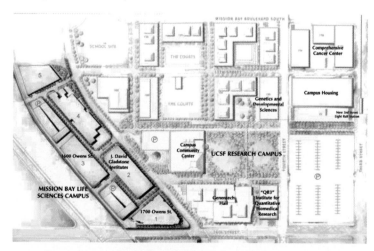

"Our goal as the developer of Mission Bay's Life Science Campus is to create a premier biomedical-research campus that will provide a one-of-a-kind environment for creativity, innovation, discovery and development," says Mike Monroe, senior vice president of commercial leasing for Catellus. "The vision is to have UCSF's faculty and students interacting with private industry on a daily basis."

COLLABORATION OPPORTUNITIES IN STATE-OF-THE-ART FACILITIES

Companies locating in the Life Sciences Campus will find an ideal environment to form basic research collaborations, conduct clinical research and trials, and participate in scientist exchange programs. Those opportunities will span more than a dozen scientific areas, including chemical, molecular and structural biology, developmental neurobiology, drug design and human genetics. Tenants will enjoy the use of UCSF's community recreation and conference center that houses a gymnasium, an indoor swimming pool, a computer library and restaurants.

In late 2004, the J. David Gladstone Institute will move into a new, 180,000 square-foot facility directly across from the UCSF campus, where Gladstone researchers hold faculty appointments. There they will continue research in AIDS, cardiovascular and neurological diseases.

Life Science Campus research buildings are being designed to accommodate small to large tenants. The buildings are designed for ultimate flexibility to accommodate a wide variety of uses, including office, lab and lab support, plus highly specialized areas including manufacturing and pilot plant operations. And as part of the San Francisco enterprise zone, tenants can take advantage of significant tax incentives.

Mission Bay: A great place to live, work, play and discover. ■

Catellus Development Corp.
255 Channel St.
San Francisco, CA 94118
Tel: 415-355-6643
Mike_Monroe@catellus.com
www.missionbaysf.com

Burrill & Company

For more than 35 years, G. Steven Burrill has helped shape the future of the life sciences. As advocate, promoter, believer and supporter, Burrill has been an architect of biotech business from the very beginning.

In the late 1960s, Burrill first nurtured entrepreneurs from his post at Ernst & Young (E & Y, previously Arthur Young E & Y) where by the end of his tenure he was worldwide chair of the manufacturing/high technology group. He helped start, from the dining room table in some cases, several leading companies in the industry; businesses that would later become Chiron, Amgen and Genentech. His collaboration, in 1968, with Alex Zaffaroni brought ALZA into existence; 18 months ago, Johnson & Johnson paid $12.5 billion for the company.

When Burrill retired from E & Y at the end of 1993, he was their lead partner in the high-tech/biotech world responsible for about one third of the company's $6.5 billion in business. Yet, as astounding as it seems, it's what he's done in his retirement that has cemented his status as guru of the biotechnology industry.

Without even taking a day off from work, Burrill opened shop at Burrill & Company (B & C) on January 1, 1994, to concentrate his efforts in the life sciences. Explaining the passion behind his work in human health care, he admits, "It felt a lot better to go home at the end of the day after helping to cure AIDS or fight cancer than it did making money on the Internet."

At first, Burrill intended to help build a few health care or pharmaceutical organizations as he had at E & Y, but he soon found himself perfectly positioned for a role in strategic alliances. He knew virtually everyone in biotech, but a lot of the big players in the industry did not know one another. Already a member of the board-of-directors at several companies, Burrill was primed to strategically align partnerships. Then, between 1997-1998, he expanded the capital components of Burrill & Company to include the venture capital business.

In its 10th year, Burrill & Company is a life sciences merchant bank with 45 associates in its businesses: venture capital and strategic partnering. What differentiates B & C from most venture capital firms is how the company accumulates capital. Most VCs gather funds solely from institutional investors such as big pension plans. For B & C, however, resources come, for the most part, from the private sector: 22 of the largest companies in the world, including Nestlé, Aventis, Bayer, ADM, Chiron, DSM, Degussa, IBM, Novo and Unilever, are among Burrill & Company's limited partners.

Another factor giving B & C the competitive edge is its approach to investing in the life sciences. "We have a more

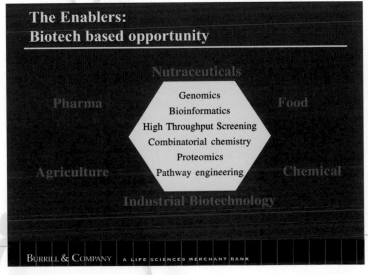

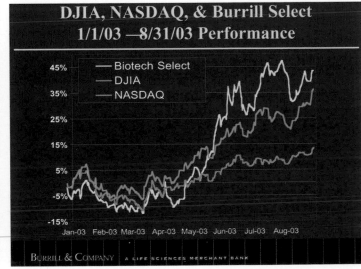

MBT Architecture

Bay Area Biotech

For the past 50 years, MBT has applied passion, leadership and creativity in setting a high standard for design in the Bay Area and beyond.

Clients and peers have publicly acknowledged the firm's excellence. MBT has won more than 60 design awards, including five National AIA Honor Awards and five R&D Magazine *Lab of the Year* Awards, including the Stowers Institute for Medical Research in 2002 (top-right photo). MBT has also received awards for interior design and innovative applications of simple construction technologies and inexpensive building materials.

Work for Chevron in Richmond led to MBT's first *Lab of the Year* award, and the IBM Santa Teresa campus received an AIA National Honor Award. Other key Bay Area clients include Stanford University, UCSF, UC Berkeley, six other UC campuses and both Lawrence Livermore and Lawrence Berkeley Laboratories.

As biotech evolved out of academia, MBT became lab designers for a new industry. Early work included projects for

Genentech and Cetus (now Chiron). Recent projects reflect the firm's broad base and also include Applied Biosystems' new Pleasanton campus, Bio-Rad's expansion in Hercules and Genencor's Technology Center in Palo Alto, another *Lab of the Year* award winner (bottom-right photo). MBT has also successfully served major pharmaceutical companies, including Bayer, Alza, Syntex (now Roche) and Merck.

MBT brings benefits of the corporate and development sectors to academia. These benefits include innovation in the delivery process, cost control and efficient building technology. In addition, it brings the signatures of academia — discovery, interaction and campus environments — to assist the

corporate users in attracting and retaining top talent. According to Bryan Croeni, MBT principal and member of the Bay Area Bioscience Center's board of directors, "There are firms who are strong in either academic or corporate projects. MBT is distinguished by strength in both areas, and clients in both sectors benefit by our deep and diverse experience."

One of MBT's key projects illustrates this strength: Stanford University's innovative multi-disciplinary Clark Center (left photo), which was designed in collaboration with Foster & Partners. An innovative and fast-paced project-delivery process enabled design and construction to proceed concurrently.

The Clark Center's innovative planning solution enables researchers from engineering, medicine, humanities and social science to work together effectively to solve problems. "The intention was to break the mold," says Russ Drinker, MBT's CEO. "When one group completes its research, the area can be easily changed to accommodate the needs of a different research group."

MBT's innovative approach to design enabled the firm to win the design competition for the Northern California Institute for Research and Education's new 200,000-gsf medical research building. The 5-story building, situated at the Veteran's Affairs San Francisco campus will feature laboratories, offices and a conference center to support the mission of the organization.

As MBT embarks on its second half-century, MBT continues to bring the firm's hallmarks of innovation and resourcefulness to its academic and commercial clients, creating world-class buildings for the Bay Area and beyond. ■

MBT Architecture
info@mbtarch.com
www.mbtarch.com

MRBiotech
Staffing Specialists to the Biotech Industry

For fifteen years, MRBiotech has successfully provided technical, managerial and executive talent to the biotech industry. In many cases, MRBiotech has been in the biotech business longer than the clients it serves.

Their commitment to this emerging industry is evident in their work with more than 75 satisfied, Bay Area biotech businesses, more than 125 world wide. MRBiotech has helped find the "needle in the haystack" that many companies need to succeed in the laboratory, the plant, in the clinic or the marketplace

Most executive recruiting firms represent a wide array of industries. In such firms, those recruiters who "specialize" in biotechnology today might have worked with candidates, only a few months earlier, in an industry as far removed from biotechnology as, say, automobile manufacturing or plastics.

MRBiotech's exclusive focus on biotechnology is the key to its success. When an MRBiotech recruiter works with a director of clinical affairs at a biotech company, that company has access to all of the resources an expert recruiter in clinical affairs has to offer. MRBiotech knows biotech's key players, those destined to be movers and shakers in the industry, and those who already are.

MRBiotech's specialized focus in no way implies a narrow point of view. **Recruiters at MRBiotech place candidates in a number of disciplines — research, development, informatics, quality assurance, engineering, regulatory, clinical, manufacturing and business development — and in a wide variety of positions within each discipline.** Scientists with international reputations, for instance, are placed at pre-IPO startups while regulatory or clinical specialists are introduced to career-enhancing opportunities at *Fortune* 500 companies.

Keeping costs down in an executive search means finding the right candidates, at the right time and in the right place. MRBiotech's extensive database of California's biotech workforce offers clients a competitive advantage. Whenever possible, local candidates are presented to a client in order to decrease the costs, time and uncertainty relocation may introduce.

When a long-distance candidate is the right person for the job, however, MRBiotech's affiliation with Management Recruiters International (MRI), the world's largest search organization, allows our clients access to additional resources such as nationwide videoconferencing for candidate interviews, as well as complete relocation services across the country or around the world.

"We know the Bay Area," says Mark Hoffman, MRBiotech's owner and manager. "Given the complexities of the area — its climate and microclimates, housing costs, commute patterns, educational systems and politics — placing an outside candidate here can be a challenge." Hoffman says, "We find and place professionals who not only adjust, but thrive in their new home and work environments. MRI's network of recruiters in all fields often helps find employment for spouses employed in other industries."

MRBiotech takes pride in knowing its efforts are improving the careers of many of its candidates, while at the same time contributing to the success of many of its client companies, some of which it has helped build since their initial days as a start-up.

"Finding a technically qualified person is the easiest part of our job," Hoffman explains. "What sets us apart from other recruiting firms is our ability to find candidates who are motivated to make a change, compatible with the client company culture and, if necessary, willing to relocate a family."

"This is what an experienced, professional recruiting firm is able to do," Hoffman adds. ■

MRBiotech
2354 Powell St., Ste.A
Emeryville, CA 94608
510-658-1405
FAX: 510-658-1428
www.MRBiotech.com

Nektar Therapeutics

Founded in 1990 when John Patton and Bob Platz left their respective posts at Genentech and SRI, Nektar Therapeutics in San Carlos has gone far beyond its original goal of providing inhalable technologies for drugs that were formerly deliverable through injection only.

In the late 1990s, when pharmaceutical and biotechnology companies were increasingly in need of innovative drug-delivery systems to improve and extend their products, Nektar continued to improve its inhalation methods and added advanced injectable and oral drug-delivery methods to its portfolio. Nektar did this by acquiring companies with advanced PEGylation and supercritical fluid technologies.

In Nektar's pulmonary delivery solutions, macromolecule and small molecule drugs that are generally delivered via needle are transported to the bloodstream through a breath. Nektar's inhalable technologies allow for a localized treatment of lung diseases that results in the use of less drug than is necessary through injection. This provides faster delivery onset than provided through most oral or injection methods.

Nektar's flagship product from its inhalable platform is in late stage clinical trials. Exubera®, an inhalable insulin product, is being developed by Pfizer and their partner Aventis. "We are working in partnership with Chiron," says Joyce Strand, director of corporate communications at Nektar, "to use our technology to treat the lung directly. We are also partnering with other companies to enable the rapid delivery of drugs for indications (migraine headaches or allergies) where getting medication to the bloodstream quickly is vital to the success of the treatment."

Nektar's second technology platform, its advanced PEGylation solution, improves the injection process by weighing molecules down so that after entry into the bloodstream, drugs remain in the system longer and resist immune reaction.

Five of Nektar's PEGylated drugs have received FDA approval and are on the market. PEGASYS®, a product from Roche, allows patients with hepatitis C to benefit from fewer injections over a shorter treatment period. And Amgen's product Neulasta™ extends the life cycle of Amgen's NEUPOGEN® line by using Nektar's PEGylation technology to treat neutrapenia. Another Nektar product, Macugen™, developed by Eyetech to treat macular degeneration and licensed by Pfizer, is in late stage trials. Macugen™ puts good use to advances in the drug-delivery process by requiring fewer injections directly into the eye.

Nektar's third technology, particle engineering, employs supercritical fluid processing to better control the shape and size of particles in powdered drugs. In the early stages of development, this solution allows drug products to move from inception to production more efficiently.

While other companies in the drug delivery realm are now moving into drug discovery, Nektar remains committed to its expertise in delivery. "If you focus on just one drug," Strand says about the standard drug discovery process, "you expend an enormous amount of resources on what can be a very risky situation. In our model, with the same amount of dollars and with funding from our partners, we can help develop as many as ten products."

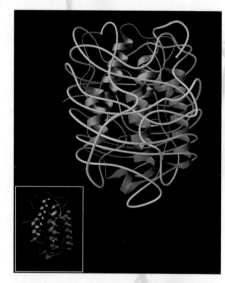

"We do take some drugs through Phase I or Phase II trials to demonstrate the viability of the products," Strand explains. "Then our partners complete late stage development, and market and sell the products."

"Drug delivery technologies can and will make a difference in the development of new and better medicines," Strand adds. Nektar's commitment to collaborative research and development guarantees that the drug delivery company in San Carlos will continue to pioneer those technologies that make medicine better. ∎

Nektar Therapeutics
150 Industrial Rd.
San Carlos, CA 94070
650-631-3100
Fax: 650-631-3150
www.nektar.com

Novozymes Biotech Inc.

When Denmark-based Novozymes A/S was in search of a U.S. home to advance its enzyme research, Davis, CA seemed the perfect place to set up shop. In 1992, when the company opened its doors only 70 miles from San Francisco in a town that hosts a University of California campus, the Davis unit called Novozymes Biotech became an integral part of the company's scientific laboratory and business development centers.

As the world's largest producer of enzymes, Novozymes finds itself part of almost every industry there is. "Everyday you eat, wear, or use something made with our enzymes," says Glenn Nedwin, Novozymes Biotech president. "Our products are found or used in detergents, starch processing, textiles, food, beverages, animal feed, personal care items, and the pulp and paper industry. The list goes on and on. Our products are best characterized as biological and environmentally friendly solutions to industrial problems."

In 1941, Novozymes (formerly a division of Novo Nordisk) created the commercial use of enzymes. Since then, Novozymes has introduced almost every major class of enzyme into the market. Currently, the core of our business is in industrial enzymes, but, "in the future, we'd like to get our newly formed industrial microorganisms and biopharmaceuticals units to become significant part of our overall business-to-business strategy," Nedwin says.

Novozymes plans to continue its leadership of the world market through its manufacturing practices and innovative technologies. With manufacturing centers in Denmark, U.S. (N.C.), China, and Brazil, the company's capability for large-scale fermentation sets up significant barriers for competition.

With more than 4200 patents, Novozymes also relies on its proprietary products, fermentation, and recombinant DNA technologies to keep the company strong. "We have the capacity to harness proteins in their environments and also create new molecules when we can't find them in nature," Nedwin says. "We use technologies similar to the ones that pharmaceutical companies use, but we apply them to the industrial area."

In 2001, Novozymes received a $14.8 million dollar subcontract from the U. S. Department Energy to discover more economical ways to produce ethanol from biomass, an alternative energy source that would help the world be less dependent on oil.

"Today, ethanol is made primarily from corn starch. We are looking to help create the formation of a new industry by converting biomass, what's left over such as the corn stalks, the cobs, and anything else made out of cellulose, into glucose, which can then be fermented into ethanol and other high value products," Nedwin says.

Its enzymes and ethanol projects are only a tiny component of Novozymes' commitment to its communities. "We are one of the few companies in the world that adheres to reporting on financial, environmental, and social responsibility-the triple bottom line," Nedwin boasts.

Last year, Novozymes received first place among all biotechnology companies in the Dow Jones Sustainability Indexes. "Novozymes is a company that really cares about these issues, and our employees feel great about the company's values and mission," he adds. ■

Novozymes Biotech, Inc.
1445 Drew Avenue
Davis, CA 95616
Telephone: 530-757-8100
Facsimile: 530-758-0317
www.novozymesbiotech.com
www.novozymes.com

Pelikan Technologies

For almost three decades now, home glucose-testing devices have been available, but during this period patients have struggled with two demons: pain and paraphernalia. The pain resulted from the difficulty of obtaining a small sample of blood for the glucose test, as the sample usually came from their fingertips. The sample was obtained by piercing the skin with a lancing device, which commonly required a launcher. In use, the lancet was inserted in the launcher, the launcher cocked and then fired to force the lancet into the fingertip to produce a drop of blood. Unfortunately, all this effort often resulted in pain and no blood, in which case the process had to be repeated all over again on another fingertip.

Then there was the glucose meter to contend with. The drop of blood had to be put on a strip and the strip had to be inserted into the meter to obtain a reading, without the blood touching anything. Of course, the meter needed calibration every now and then, otherwise the patient could not be certain that it was giving valid readings. The calibrator was a fluid in a small bottle, which also had to be carried along with all the other pieces and disposables. All of the paraphernalia was bad enough for adults, but even more daunting for children.

Pelikan Technologies is designing two products to simplify life for people with diabetes. The second, due in 2005, is a radically new glucose meter. Radical in the sense that everything a patient needs is already in the meter. The meter has a tiny disposable disk, which, contains everything needed for 50 measurements. Everything. No separate launchers, lancets, strips or calibrators. To use, the device is pressed against the patient's fingertip, the patient presses a button and then simply reads the blood-glucose measurement on the display. There is

nothing to assemble or discard — in short, it is the first totally integrated device. Furthermore, it will get the blood sample almost every time, and with much less pain than other devices on the market today.

Pelikan's first product, unveiled at the June 2003 meeting of the American Diabetes Association, is essentially the same device minus the glucose measuring capability. This device, named the Pelikan Sun™, is the most advanced lancing system available. It, too, carries all of the disposables required by a patient for 50 measurements. This equates to about two weeks' use for heavy users and a month or so for those who test only once a day. The disposables are sealed in a small disk that is easily replaced.

The technology for these products was first conceived at HP Laboratories in Palo Alto. The work continued when a segment of HP separated and became known as Agilent Technologies. Agilent later spun off a small company, Pelikan Technologies, which is dedicated to bringing the technology to children and adults with diabetes. The rest, as they say, is history.

Dirk Boecker, MD, PhD, the company's co-founder, president and CEO is very proud of the company's progress: "Pelikan's design is radical because it was conceived by starting with a study of the human skin and not as an add-on to some existing glucose meter product. Our devices are particularly suited to children with diabetes, who often have sensitive skin and therefore benefit the most from our advances in technology." ∎

Pelikan Technologies Inc.
1072 East Meadow Circle
Palo Alto, CA 94303
650-842-1000
Fax 650-842-1039
www.pelikantechnologies.com

Rudolph and Sletten, Inc.
Building biotechnology, one brick at a time

It all started in a garage in 1960 when Onslow "Rudy" Rudolph noticed a growing demand for special clean rooms within manufacturing plants. He told his boss at San Francisco contractors Williams and Burroughs that he'd like to create a niche business building clean rooms and asked if he could take a colleague, Ken Sletten, with him.

"Dad saw an evolving need inside these high-tech plants that were being built," says Rudy's son, Allen Rudolph, a fifth-generation contractor who is president and CEO of Rudolph and Sletten, Inc., the premier biopharmaceutical and biotech general contracting firm on the West Coast.

Starting in the Rudolph's garage with one pickup truck and two employees, they began building the expertise to fill that niche and soon racked up a list of projects with the pioneers of high-tech. Through the 1960s, they built plants for Fairchild Semiconductor, Lockheed Missiles & Space Company, Memorex and Hewlett-Packard, among others. Soon they would add Sun Microsystems, Xerox and Watson Laboratories.

As Silicon Valley grew, so did the firm's expertise, making it the obvious choice when the biotech industry began. Starting again with the pioneers, the firm built a client list of the leaders of biotechnology and science, among them ALZA, Johnson & Johnson, Cell Genesys, Raven Biotechnologies, Genentech, AMGEN, Chiron, Bayer, the Lucille Packard Children's Hospital and the Monterey Bay Aquarium Research Institute.

"Constructing office buildings is profitable, but it's not that rewarding," Rudolph says. "Doing work for Stanford or the biotech and pharmaceutical companies is different — when we work on a building and a cancer treatment comes out of that lab, we feel like we're part of the cure."

Today, Rudolph and Sletten has more than 800 employees and is the nation's 24th largest general building contractor, with headquarters in Foster City and regional offices in Roseville, Irvine and San Diego. Along the way, it has built a reputation for honest dealing, fair pricing and a commitment to the highest quality projects.

Delivering those values starts with the crew. To maintain its expertise in-house, the firm has hired 500 skilled tradesmen. Some are third-generation tradesmen, others have been with the firm for two decades; all have been hand-picked for their professional and technical expertise.

That level of experience has taught project team members to get the

plan right before breaking ground, which is why Rudolph and Sletten employs twice as many estimators as its competitors. Rudolph says one of the firm's greatest strengths is in preconstruction - estimating how much the job will cost, building life-size mockups of the final plan and helping clients figure out exactly what is needed. As a result, he says, "Clients trust us with their unique and challenging projects."

That eye for excellence has led to an 85 percent client return rate, including ongoing projects stemming from its original work for David Packard Sr. And, like Packard himself, the firm has always believed in giving back. That includes donating to a number of community service endeavors, such as providing a crane and operator for Habitat for Humanity projects — year after year — or helping remodel women's shelters and drug treatment centers.

"Because we have limited our geographic expansion, we're active in supporting our local communities," Rudolph says. "It's important that our company give back to the community so that the community, in turn, can grow and prosper. We firmly believe this is the best way to ensure the highest quality of life for future generations. Ken Sletten started the tradition of corporate philanthropy with a strong commitment to community involvement, and we've kept it up for more than 40 years." ■

Rudolph and Sletten, Inc.
General and Engineering Contractors
989 East Hillsdale Blvd., Ste. 100
Foster City, CA 94404
650-572-1919
Fax: 650-574-9153
www.rsconstruction.com

Thermo Finnigan

Thermo Electron Corporation offers integrated laboratory solutions, including state-of-the-art instrument systems, advanced software and HPLC column technology. These solutions offer a wide range of innovative phases and hardware designs, tailored to meet the rigorous demands of lab professionals in applications such as proteomics, drug discovery, environmental analysis and analytical quantitation. Thermo manufactures mass spectrometry and chromatography systems, among the most accurate and sensitive available, for analyzing a wide array of substances.

"We're among the market leaders in the industry, assisting biotechnology and pharmaceutical companies with their drug discovery process," says Dr. Iain Mylchreest, general manager of the San Jose, Calif., manufacturing facility. "Our ion trap mass spectrometers are important tools used to analyze proteins, as well as small molecule drugs."

These instruments aid laboratory professionals, often by automating the process of separating, identifying and quantifying natural products, chemical mixtures and biological samples. The robust nature and extreme sensitivity of the Finnigan LCQ™ Deca XP Plus ion trap mass spectrometer makes it the industry standard for research applications and complex analysis. As the most sensitive MSn analytical instrument, it is tailor-made to analyze impurities.

The Finnigan ProteomeX™ Workstation is a fully integrated, multidimensional capillary LC/MS system based on the ultra-sensitive LCQ Deca XP Plus ion trap mass spectrometer, Surveyor HPLC and BioWorks software. ProteomeX is designed and optimized for LC/MS/MS experiments. The system is installed to meet multidimensional LC/MS/MS performance criteria so that a researcher will immediately be able

to run meaningful experiments required for proteomics, such as high-throughput protein identification, shotgun sequencing of complex samples and differential protein quantification. Operation of this powerful system has been greatly simplified without compromising performance. ProteomeX facilitates easy method set-up and execution, in addition to automatic identification of peptides and proteins with the proven BioWorks™ software package.

The Finnigan TSQ® Quantum platform has been expanded into three application-specific instruments, providing life scientists integrated LC-MS/MS and software solutions for every stage of the drug development process. The flagship, Finnigan TSQ Quantum Ultra, offers the widest linear dynamic range and highest sensitivity of any triple quadruple mass spectrometer. It is the premier instrument for pre-clinical and clinical quantification.

"We continuously push the boundaries of technology in order to provide our customers with the most advanced analytical instruments and solutions," Mylchreest explains. "Thermo enables companies to make scientific breakthroughs faster and more efficiently."

Approximately 350 scientists, engineers, manufacturing technicians, managers and administrative personnel are employed at the San Jose facility, which manufactures liquid chromatography and life science mass spectrometry products. Thermo Electron has revenues of more than $2 billion and employs approximately 11,000 people in 30 countries worldwide. ∎

Thermo Electron
355 River Oaks Pkwy.
San Jose, CA 95134
408-965-6000
www.thermo.com

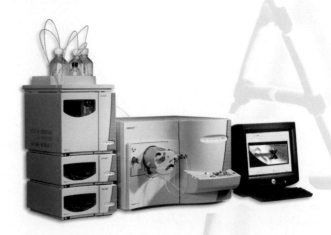

Roche Molecular Systems Inc.
Celebrating 20 years of PCR innovation

W hen Severe Acute Respiratory Syndrome (SARS) broke out in China in early 2003, it caught the medical community by surprise. A quick diagnosis was critical in preventing a global epidemic, yet no test existed for the disease.

At Roche Molecular Systems Inc. (RMS), diagnostic scientists immediately set to work, collaborating closely with virology institutes and government agencies worldwide. Within a mere eight weeks — the shortest development time ever for a Roche research product — they had created a research product based on state-of-the-art polymerase chain reaction (PCR) technology.

"That's one of our strengths," says RMS Chief Executive Officer Heiner Dreismann, PhD. "We pride ourselves on having the technology, flexibility and partnerships that are needed to respond rapidly to global health issues."

That rapid response has defined the company since its inception. Formed in 1991 using technology developed at Cetus Corp., which is located in Emeryville, RMS has invested hundreds of millions of dollars in the ensuing decade to accelerate the development of PCR technology, with an emphasis on practical applications with direct benefits to health care.

As a result, the company has been first in its field to create simple laboratory diagnostics that we now take for granted. Among them were the first test for *Chlamydia* in 1992, the first viral load test for HIV in 1996 and, more recently, the blood screening test for the West Nile Virus, which is currently an Investigational Use Only product approved for clinical studies under an Investigational New Drug Application.

USING DNA FOR DIAGNOSIS

All of those tests are based on PCR, a Nobel-prize winning technology that was first described in the journal *Science* in 1985. Since then, Roche Molecular Systems has helped that technology become one of the most widely used techniques in molecular biology.

"We were the first company to commercialize PCR technology, and the first to get FDA approval for a diagnostic test using this technology," Dreismann explains. "Since then, we've been working closely with the medical and research community to establish PCR as the gold standard in the field of diagnostics."

Essentially a process of DNA replication, PCR technology enables scientists to use genetic samples as small as one cell — whether from hair, blood, skin or saliva — to produce a large enough quantity of DNA to analyze.

To date, PCR technology has been used in a wide variety of different assays, from medicine to agriculture to law to studying ancient DNA from fossils. Among its uses are diagnosing specific genetic conditions or illnesses, predicting how well an individual will respond to a medication, identifying viruses, connecting an individual to a crime, establishing paternity and determining the identity of a deceased person.

It has very quickly become an essential tool for improving human health in such critical areas as diagnosing infectious disease.

BEST AND THE BRIGHTEST

In just over a decade, Roche Molecular Systems has established itself as the recognized leader in the development of molecular-based tests, as well as the automated testing platforms to analyze them. Based in Pleasanton, Roche Molecular

Systems is one of five business areas of Roche Diagnostics, located in Basel, Switzerland, and is responsible for the research, development, manufacture and marketing of PCR-based products.

RMS has nearly 900 employees in the United States, half of whom are in the Bay Area, and another 220 in Germany and Switzerland. As a result, RMS is graced with the dual advantage of the agility and presence of a local, mid-sized research company and the stability and strength of its Swiss parent, F. Hoffmann-La Roche Ltd., a world leader in research-based health care.

RMS focuses on six PCR businesses: virology, blood screening, microbiology, genomics, oncology and women's health. Those businesses serve a wide variety of audiences, from medical laboratories to doctors' offices and industry. In the Bay Area, the Pleasanton facility focuses on the production and marketing of *in vitro* diagnostic products, while scientists at the Alameda facility are involved with new markers in infectious diseases, microbiology, genetics and genetic improvements on the next generation of *in vitro* tests.

The science relies on a powerful staff to keep it going. Its research team alone boasts more than 1,300 years of collective experience, and the RMS senior management team has an average tenure of 10 years with the company.

"The level of expertise we have under our roof is what really sets us apart," Dreismann says. "Our vision has always focused on keeping the best and the brightest people by fostering innovative work, treating them well and sharing in a mission to improving health around the world."

AUTOMATED FUTURE

Central to that mission is the pioneering spirit that led Roche into the PCR technology in the first place. Today, the company remains committed to pioneering new ways to use PCR to diagnose disease and monitor response to therapy, as well as helping physicians better assess their choice of therapy.

Roche is also pioneering advances in instrumentation for PCR testing, which is becoming smaller, more automated and easier for a wider variety of laboratories to use. In essence, it is the company's goal to help put molecular technology in virtually every laboratory.

"PCR technology has created a revolutionary potential for new approaches to medicine," Dreismann says. "Our hope is that someday doctors will be able to use the molecular information we are gathering now to understand and predict diseases that we don't normally consider to be genetic conditions — like osteoporosis and heart disease — and prevent them before they occur." ∎

Roche Molecular Systems Inc.
4300 Hacienda Dr.
Pleasanton, CA 94588-2722
925-730-8300
Fax: 925-225-0369
www.roche-diagnostics.com

Siemens

Siemens Medical Solutions: Oncology and Ultrasound

Siemens — more than likely, you've heard the name before. In fact, across the world people are familiar with Siemens Corporation and its "global network of innovation." With offices in more than 190 countries, Siemens employs 70,000 people in the United States alone. On a worldwide basis, Siemens encompasses much of what is thought of today as business. In California, Siemens operates in the power generation, communications, transportation and medical technology sectors. And Siemens Medical Solutions, with world headquarters of two of its global business divisions in the Bay Area, is a shining star among Siemens business groups.

As the world's largest supplier of clinical and information technologies, Siemens Medical Solutions offers a comprehensive spectrum of equipment and services to address the needs of patients around the world. Diagnostic and treatment technologies range from conventional X-ray, ultrasound, CT, MR, PET and PET/CT molecular imaging to linear accelerators and ultrasound-guided brachytherapy.

ONCOLOGY CARE SYSTEMS

With global headquarters in Concord, the Oncology Care Systems Division of Siemens Medical Solutions USA is a world leader in cancer treatment systems. "In a country where, each year, more than 1.3 million people acquire some form of cancer," explains Dr. Ajit Singh, president of oncology Care Systems, "it is imperative to produce innovative technology and solutions for health care." Every day in the United States alone, more than 30,000 cancer patients are treated via Siemens radiation therapy systems, an indispensable tool in the fight against the disease.

With a workforce of 360 employees locally and more than 1,500 globally, Oncology Care Systems designs, manufactures, markets and supports its signature product, the medical linear accelerator, and oncology-specific software solutions.

Introduced in 2002, the ONCOR™ Linear Accelerator is Siemens newest treatment delivery system. It is designed to

incorporate the newest technological features as well as information platforms, such as the COHERENCE™ Oncology Workspaces, a suite of user-centric software applications for the oncologist, physicist, dosimetrist and therapist. Our PRIMUS® Linear Accelerator, debuted in 1996, is installed today in cancer care facilities worldwide. Both systems are capable of Intensity Modulated Radiation Therapy (IMRT), a treatment technique that allows for the automatic, sequential delivery of concentrated doses of radiation over shorter periods of treatment, making the fight against cancer potentially more successful and less draining.

"Siemens is the only linear accelerator manufacturer to also offer a full line of imaging and diagnostic modalities. We are committed to providing high quality, well-integrated Oncology Workflow Solutions™ for prevention and screening through diagnosis, staging, treatment delivery and follow-up," Dr. Singh adds.

ULTRASOUND DIVISION

The Bay Area is also home to the Ultrasound Division of Siemens Medical Solutions. Siemens moved its ultrasound headquarters to Mountain View in November 2000 after acquiring ACUSON Corporation, a leading manufacturer and service provider of medical diagnostic ultrasound systems. ACUSON was founded in 1979 by former Hewlett-Packard engineers.

The Ultrasound Division proudly offers the most comprehensive portfolio in ultrasound equipment. The diversity of products Siemens provides only complements the quality of care they

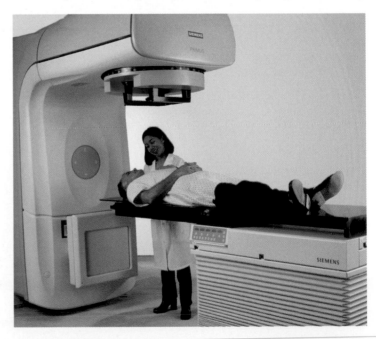

The PRIMUS Linear Accelerator delivers precision megavoltage X-rays and electron beams for cancer treatment.

John Pavlidis

Ajit Singh, Ph. D.

offer. According to third-party consultants, the ACUSON Sequoia™ ultrasound platform, manufactured in Mountain View, has been the best selling ultrasound device nationwide for the past five years.

"The ACUSON Sequoia system has defined a new market segment in ultra-premium ultrasound," says John Pavlidis, president of the Siemens Medical Solutions Ultrasound Division. "It provides new value and performance points and covers the entire spectrum of ultrasound applications: radiology, cardiology, OB/GYN, vascular, breast and surgery imaging."

Based on proprietary technology, ACUSON Sequoia system is based on a new method to create the ultrasound image. Unlike other ultrasound systems that produce images from only amplitude information, ACUSON Sequoia system uses all available diagnostic data, phase and amplitude, to form representations of tissue. Users can now routinely see anatomy and physiology not generally seen with conventional ultrasound, which results in better tissue differentiation in the body, especially between healthy and diseased tissue.

Another technological breakthrough has been the ACUSON AcuNav™ diagnostic ultrasound catheter. "We are the only company to manufacture a high resolution ultrasound imaging catheter used for cardiology diagnostics," Pavlidis reports. "There is no competitive product providing such excellent image quality."

Products manufactured by the Ultrasound Division undoubtedly benefit the patients they help treat. More surprising is the protection they afford a health-care provider. "Unlike most medical equipment, ultrasound generates a hands-on interaction between patient and technician," explains Pavlidis. "We focus on improving the ergonomic factors of our systems to minimize repetitive stress and create a user-friendly tool for health-care providers."

These high standards are duly recognized. The ACUSON and SONOLINE® product lines have received multiple excellence-in-design awards from, among others, the Industrial Designers Society of America and Business Week.

SIEMENS: LOCAL AND GLOBAL

Given their relative proximity, the Ultrasound Division and Oncology Care Systems are in a unique position to collaborate. Capitalizing on the commitment each company has made to fight cancer and stand behind the community, the two organizations have teamed up to sponsor the San Francisco Race for the Cure. In supporting this Bay Area tradition, Siemens Medical Solutions helps to raise money for breast cancer research, adding a local element to its global fight against the many forms of the disease.

While the company's civic and economic contributions to the Bay Area are clear, both Siemens divisions reap rewards from the community as well. "Our locations in the Bay Area allow us access to excellent and diverse talent from all over the world," Dr. Singh says. "Diversity and Siemens go hand in hand."

Beyond the practical benefits of belonging to a thriving community, these two members of the Siemens Medical Solutions family are rewarded with the knowledge that their solutions advance medical technology and provide hope and relief to those battling disease all over the world. ■

Siemens Medical Solutions USA Inc.
Oncology Care Systems
4040 Nelson Ave., Concord, CA 94520
925-246-8200
Fax: 925-602-8066
www.SiemensMedical.com/oncology

Siemens Medical Solutions USA Inc.
Ultrasound Division
1230 Shorebird Way, Mountain View, CA 94039
650-969-9112
Fax: 650-968-1833
www.SiemensMedical.com
www.ultrasound.com

Siemens Medical Solutions that help

The ACUSON Sequoia system covers the entire spectrum of ultrasound applications.

Stratagem Healthcare Communications

When Stratagem Healthcare Communications opened shop in 1997, founders Paul Harris, Susan Hempstead and Patricia Malone knew they could deliver the creative and strategic expertise of a large advertising agency with the flexibility, nimbleness and personalized attention typically expected from smaller shops. Their goal past and present is to create a more streamlined alternative to the time-consuming hierarchies in healthcare communications.

"One main point that differentiates Stratagem from competitors is that we hire senior-level talent," says Malone, principal and creative director at the San Francisco-based company. "Stratagem team members bring a depth of experience from major pharmaceutical companies, Madison Avenue advertising agencies and the practical side of healthcare delivery, making it possible for the company to deliver a breadth of offerings for pharmaceutical, biotech, diagnostic and device, and personal care products," she explains. "We try to create teams with experience in almost every category so that there's almost no ramp-up time after we learn the culture of a particular client." What's the outcome for Stratagem clients trying to reach the market as quickly as possible? The right message for the right audience, right on time.

Stratagem develops campaigns for pharmaceutical products ranging from anti-depressants and anti-infectives to cardiovascular drugs and local analgesics. In the diagnostics and devices area, Stratagem routinely works on projects for products that screen for cancer, monitor blood gas, produce echocardiographs and treat acne. In personal care, the agency has helped brand products in areas as wide-ranging as oral health, hypertension, allergy medications and incontinence care. The company's diversity also extends to its methods of communication and media placement as Stratagem provides coverage through print, broadcast, Web, direct mail and collateral materials. This year, the company was named among *Med Ad News'* top 50 healthcare agencies and, according to the *San Francisco Business Times*, among the top 100 fastest growing companies in the Bay Area.

Healthcare advertising differs from pure consumer advertising in general with regard to the language used to communicate to target audiences. "Although we are still working with consumers when we work in the professional healthcare arena," Malone says, "the mass selling approach does not necessarily work. We know, for instance, that we won't be speaking to a cardiovascular surgeon the same way we talk to a drug discovery

It's time to shine.

Your challenges are multi-faceted. But so is our expertise. In fact, we have decades of senior-level experience in meeting marketing challenges of every size and shape. Whether it's pharmaceuticals, diagnostics, devices or personal care products, we believe it's important to get our hands dirty—from both a big-picture perspective and in the seemingly smallest, process-oriented tasks that can make or break a deadline (or a brand). At Stratagem, our experience means that we get to the answer faster. And we continually put the pressure on ourselves to give it a stunning final form. If your brand could shine brighter, give us a call today. Because Stratagem could be the perfect setting for your strategic brand communication.

Strategic thinking
with a gem of a creative product.

Stratagem

STRATAGEM HEALTHCARE COMMUNICATIONS   415.397.3667   WWW.STRATAGEM-HC.COM

ALL CARROT.   NO STICK.

Need a compelling incentive for prescribers and patients to prefer your injectable? Aradigm's advanced liquid delivery systems offer injectable performance without the pain of needle sticks – AER® for aerosols to reach the lung and systemic circulation, and Intraject® for needle-free access to the subcutaneous layer. These technologies can comfortably deliver almost any formulation, from small molecules to monoclonal antibodies. And with Aradigm's experienced development teams, partnering with us will be painless. So contact us today to find out how we can deliver healthy growth for your product.

ARADIGM

3929 POINT EDEN WAY, HAYWARD, CA 94545 | T. 510.265.9000 | F. 510.265.0277 | WWW.ARADIGM.COM

explains. "We explore with clients whether they would like to push the box lid up or keep it comfortably closed."

The Stratagem strategy emphasizes strong positioning and early branding. "Every agency goes in knowing they will give a strong strategic recommendation, do great creative, and reinforce or create the brand," Malone says. "But we provide top-level thinking through a more personalized process. It is important to us to deliver the best solution and to make the development process enjoyable for our clients."

Last year, Stratagem launched a separate division devoted to emerging drug discovery and biotech companies. "We continue to stress the importance of branding," Malone says, "and now have structured ourselves to make that possible for emerging companies.

"Some businesses bypass the branding stages, which they consider premature or too costly at the beginning of the marketing process," Malone says. "We believe a brand should be created before the business plan in order to create a consistent look-and-feel or personality for a service, product or corporate brand. By offering our services on a project basis," she emphasizes, "we can now help clients no matter what stage they enter the process and develop their identity with the future of their company in mind."

A growing number of Stratagem clients have global influence and require communications that resonate around the world. "We think of our services as "glocal," Malone adds, "global with a local implementation." Stratagem tailors messages to reflect the individual differences of each country, without diluting the brand on a local level.

By eliminating bureaucratic hassles, the Stratagem structure allows more time for its senior-level folks to custom fit every solution to the specifications of each client, product, brand and market. "We're passionate about all aspects of the business, but quality will always be our first priority." Malone says. "We provide sound solutions more efficiently than most shops because of the caliber of our talent and the ways in which we work." She adds, "We offer strategic thinking with a gem of a creative product." ■

Stratagem Healthcare Communications
461 Bush St., 4th Flr.
San Francisco, CA 94108
415-397-3667
Fax: 415-397-3668
www.stratagem-hc.com

scientist. Most consumer shops target only a specific kind of consumer, not a consumer who is also a neurosurgeon or an expert in genomics," she adds.

It is common knowledge that consumer advertising is about thinking outside the box. In healthcare advertising, however, the FDA issues regulations that, in effect, create a box in which agencies must work with their clients. "We understand the advertising requirements of the FDA, the prescribing information and the indication of each particular product," Malone says, "then we think outside the box from within the box. We try to bring the most creative approach to well-regulated areas." One example of Stratagem bringing a consumer approach to the life sciences is in its conceptual work with a gene discovery company on a campaign they called, "This Little Mouse Went to Market." "In that case, we opened the box as far as we could," Malone

sonicare
GO BEYOND
THE SURFACE
Introducing
the next generation
Sonicare Elite®
PHILIPS
sonicare
the sonic toothbrush

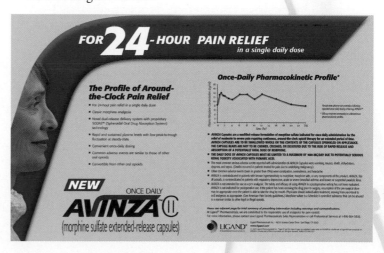

FOR 24-HOUR PAIN RELIEF
in a single daily dose

The Profile of Around-the-Clock Pain Relief

Once-Daily Pharmacokinetic Profile*

NEW
ONCE DAILY
AVINZA ℂ
(morphine sulfate extended-release capsules)

LIGAND
PHARMACEUTICALS

Townsend and Townsend and Crew LLP

Protecting the knowledge of biotechnology

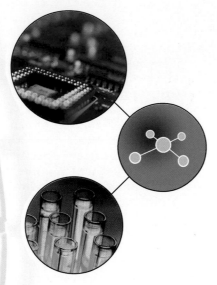

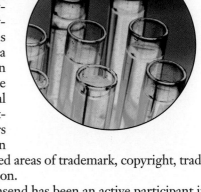

At the core of the biotechnology industry are the patents that help transform scientific advances into revenue-generating assets, making biotechnology companies attractive to investors and earning them a defensible position in the marketplace. Townsend and Townsend and Crew LLP has a long history of contributing to the growth of the biotechnology industry by working intimately with both the academic and corporate sectors to secure, assert and defend the industry's patent portfolios.

Biotechnology is an ever expanding field that now encompasses a wide array of disciplines, including diagnostic techniques, analytical techniques, pharmaceuticals, drug delivery, high-volume screening, molecular immunology, gene therapy, antisense therapy, growth-factor cloning and transgenic animals, as well as multidisciplinary areas such as nanotechnology and medical devices. With its diversified staff of technically skilled patent attorneys, Townsend has a remarkable ability to match the specialized expertise of its attorneys with the wide array of technologies in which scientific advances in biotechnology arise. This ability makes Townsend uniquely suited to provide the intellectual-property services that are so critical to the growth of this industry.

Tracing its origins back to 1860, Townsend's practice has endured and prospered through the years by continually adapting itself to meet the changing demands of intellectual property. By the 1970s, the firm, then called Townsend and Townsend, was the largest firm in the Western United States that specialized in

patents, trademarks and copyrights, and its growth has continued to the present. In 1993, Townsend and Townsend merged with Khourie, Crew and Jaeger, a firm with a nationally recognized antitrust and trial practice, to ultimately become Townsend and Townsend and Crew LLP, transforming its litigation practice into an aggressive litigation department that is renowned for its successes in intellectual property, antitrust law and commercial litigation. As a full-service law firm, Townsend has earned its reputation as a major litigation provider, in addition to being one of the most prominent intellectual property firms in the United States. Townsend offers an extensive practice in patents, as well as the related areas of trademark, copyright, trade secret and unfair competition.

In biotechnology, Townsend has been an active participant in laying the foundation for creating economic value from scientific advances, from the earliest advances in biotechnology to those emerging today. With clients ranging from small startups to multinational corporations and universities, Townsend consistently maintains its position as a leader in biotech intellectual property, numbering among its clients the two institutions with the largest public patent portfolios in the United States: the National Institutes for Health and the University of California. Townsend has 150 attorneys, of whom half are patent attorneys, many holding doctorate degrees, with expertise ranging from mechanical structures to the most sophisticated technological disciplines in physics, electronics, software, chemistry and the various specialties of biotechnology.

With a central office in San Francisco, Townsend has offices in six cities, extending from Seattle, Wash., to San Diego, Calif., with biotechnology patent attorneys in each office. The volume of patent applications prepared at Townsend is among the highest in the United States, including 624 new U.S. patent applications filed in the year 2002 alone. Townsend's biotechnology practice continues to grow at a rate of 15 percent to 20 percent per year. Currently, Townsend's chemistry and biotechnology team includes 30 patent attorneys and agents, a number that is unparalleled among West Coast firms. Recognized both locally and nationally for its expertise, skill and high-quality service, Townsend continues to be a major contributor to the biotechnology industry and a leading provider of intellectual property services. ■

Townsend and Townsend and Crew LLP
Two Embarcadero Center, 8th Flr.
San Francisco, CA 94111-3834
Tel: 415-576-0200
Fax: 415.576.0300
www.townsend.com

WHL Architects
Transforming ideas into built environments

Douglas White's entrance into the design world of biotechnology happened by circumstance in 1980. He was a young architect in a technology-focused Palo Alto architectural firm that had just won a design project for a new company up in South San Francisco, by the name of Genentech. The firm was stuck for someone to do the legwork on the project, and supervisor John Musante suggested White, who had joined the firm more than a year before.

That suggestion launched White into a field that has captivated his professional and personal interest for nearly 25 years, leading to scores of design projects in his nine years at his prior firm and the experience to build his own firm 16 years ago.

"You could say that 95 percent of my work in biotechnology through the years has evolved from that one Genentech project," White says. "I got to work with many of the early participants at Genentech and show them what an architect could do and what services we could offer. As Genentech grew and people left the company, that allowed me to follow them to other places."

As a result, White has designed projects for many of the founding companies of Bay Area bioscience, from vivaria, clean rooms and labs to the first facility for manufacturing human growth hormone. Those early projects gave him both the experience to be a valuable player in architecture and the sense of making a contribution, however small, to the greater good.

"I was absolutely caught up with biotechnology," he recalls now. "There was no one at my former firm who was very interested in it initially, but I had a real thirst to find out about the industry. I would stay after hours, scanning journals and clipping articles on it. Half the time I didn't understand what I was reading, but it ultimately helped me learn what I needed to serve the industry better."

In 1987, White decided to launch a new design firm with two other partners focusing on technology and biotech. Their goal was to create a firm in which the senior partners retained a role in every project, no matter how small. In the ensuing

years, White has transitioned both of his partners and the firm's size has adjusted with the economy, but it has remained true to that original goal.

Today, WHL has a staff of 15 in its Sunnyvale office and provides complete architectural and planning services for electronics, aerospace, biotechnology, pharmaceuticals and other technical industries. Most of those projects are in the Bay Area, but they have also been as far afield as New York, North Carolina and Florida. White is personally licensed in 10 states and NCARB accredited.

Among WHL's clients are Agilent, Amgen, Elan Pharmaceuticals, Genentech, Inamed, Kovio, Millennium Pharmaceuticals, NuGen Technologies Inc., Rigel Pharmaceuticals, Tularik and Zyomyx Inc. Many of those projects involve companies in growth mode who need an architect to not only draw up what they need now, but also to help them predict their space needs over the next decade. Providing that service requires both White's experience and his technical staff's abilities to fully analyze, estimate, schedule and document each project using the latest computer systems. It also takes a service orientation, rather than the cool-handed designer style.

What it comes down to in the end, though, is not the process, but the end product.

"I would never declare, 'This is my building,'" White says. "It's theirs. It's the penultimate compliment to have someone say, 'This is exactly what I wanted.' That's our goal with every project client." ∎

WHL Architects
250 S. Mathilda Ave.
Sunnyvale, CA 94086-6135
Tel: 408-730-9500
408-730-9588
www.whlarchitects.com

Woodruff-Sawyer & Co.
Leadership, innovation and partnership

Jerry Sullivan and Steve Sawyer

Woodruff-Sawyer & Co. understands the life science industry. For more than 15 years, it has partnered with many emerging and growing biotech and life science companies to provide insurance, risk management and employee benefits solutions. Woodruff-Sawyer's commitment to its clients is centered on adding value to the products and services it delivers.

"Woodruff-Sawyer has had a strong emphasis on technology companies going back to the birth of the Silicon Valley in the 1950s," says Steve Sawyer, executive vice president. "Focusing on the dynamics of new technology companies has definitely impacted our corporate culture. We are comfortably able to address the changing insurance needs of new and unique technologies and the people who develop them."

Woodruff-Sawyer's early involvement in the technology sector led to a corporate culture that understood how ill-suited "off the shelf" insurance products were to the newly formed and continually evolving biotech and life sciences companies. In the late 1980s, the company refused to take a "me too" approach and developed insurance products for companies involved in early-stage clinical trials. This decision altered the insurance landscape.

"Woodruff-Sawyer has demonstrated leadership in the biotech industry for many years, which few firms can match. They consistently bring innovative and creative solutions to their clients from an insurance industry that has not been known for original thinking. Furthermore, they have been committed to working with biotech companies at all stages of development, from early stage start-ups through IPO and product launch, demonstrating excellence at all stages of growth."
Scott Morrison, US Life Sciences Leader, Ernst & Young, LLP

One prime example of an insurance product that didn't address the needs of life science companies was business interruption. "The tricky part of business interruption insurance is that most of the existing coverage is designed for

profitable companies," states Jerry Lynn Sullivan, vice president. "But in the life sciences field, there are hundreds of companies and only a few that are profitable." Woodruff-Sawyer worked with the insurers to develop a product that made sense for life science companies. "Biotech companies are looking for the most effective solution and not necessarily the lowest cost product," she says.

"In my tenure at the Bay Area Bioscience Center, Woodruff-Sawyer consistently distinguished itself in its commitment to the life science industry and in bringing new ideas and creative solutions to the issues bioscience companies face."
Fred Dorey, Cooley Godward, past president, Bay Area Bioscience Center

Woodruff-Sawyer is an independent insurance brokerage providing insurance, risk management and employee benefits services and consultation to the business community. It has been selected by the Biotechnology Industry Organization (BIO) as its West-coast risk management partner. In addition, Woodruff-Sawyer was ranked the No. 1 D&O (directors and officers) broker in the nation, according to the 2002 Tillinghast-Towers Perrin annual survey. ∎

"Over the years, Woodruff-Sawyer has earned an unparalleled reputation for integrity and professionalism. Our account team has gone out of its way to retain our company's business based on performance and results, as opposed to leveraging relationships or favors. That's why they have the best reputation in the industry."
Chris Nolet, partner, Ernst & Young, LLP

Contact:
Steve Sawyer
415-399-6329
ssawyer@woodruff-sawyer.com

Jerry Lynn Sullivan
415-399-6401
jsullivan@woodruff-sawyer.com

Stan Loar, CEO, Susan Hunt, President, Dout Morton, Chairman

Index of Profiles

Index of Profiles

References

CHAPTER ONE
THE HISTORY OF BIOTECHNOLOGY

Sources:

I. *Northern California's Bioscience Legacy, BayBio, 1991.*

II. *Biotechnology in the San Francisco Bay Area, ABAG, 1987.*

III. *Biomedicine: The New Pillar in Northern California's Economy, California Healthcare Initiative, 2002.*

IV. *Alchemy to IPO, Cynthia Robbins-Roth, Pegasus, 2000.*

CHAPTER TWO
RESEARCH, INNOVATIONS & EDUCATIONAL INSTITUTIONS

Sources:

I. *PricewaterhouseCoopers MoneyTree Survey. See also "Biomedicine: The New Pillar in Northern California's Economy," the California Healthcare Institute's 2002 Report on Northern California's Biomedical R&D Industry, www.chi.org.*

II. *The Stanford Biodesign Network was originally formed as the Medical Device Network, or MDN, and was renamed in 2002 as the Stanford Biodesign Network, or BDN. BDN serves as the technology transfer and network arm of the broader Stanford Biodesign Program, http://biodesign.stanford.edu, an initiative of Stanford's Bio-X Center, http://biox.stanford.edu.*

III. *Tangible measures of "networking" are somewhat difficult to define. However, statistical analysis in March 2003 indicated that the BDN website receives at least 200 unique "hits" each week.*

IV. *Jansen, Cristina and Dillon, Harrison F. "Where do the Leads for Licenses Come From?" The Journal of the Association of University Technology Managers, Volume XI (1999). The Association of University Technology Managers, Northbrook, IL.*

V. *Companies are private and are primarily early stage. ImetRx, NeoGuide, Kerberos Proximal Solutions, VenoMatrix, StrataGent, Acumen, StemCor Systems, Inc.*

CHAPTER FOUR
PROFESSIONAL SERVICES

Footnotes:

1 *East Bay Business Times, March 17, 2003, http://eastbay.bizjournals.com/eastbay/stories/2003/03/17/focus5.html.*

2 *See Bay Area Bioscience Center, http://www.bayareabioscience.org/historyofbiotech.pdf; see also California Healthcare Institute, http://www.chi.org/home/template5.php?pid=263.*

3 *US CONST. art. I. § 8.*

4 *See Jacqueline D. Wright, Implications of Recent Patent Law Changes on Biotechnology Research and the Biotechnology Industry, 1 Va. J.L. & Tech. 2 (1997).*

5 *US Patent No. 4,237,224 (issued December 2, 1980); U.S. Patent No. 4,468,464 (issued August 28, 1984); U.S. Patent No. 4,740,470 (issued April 26, 1988).*

6 *Biotechnology at 25: The Founders, at http://bancroft.berkeley.edu/Exhibits/Biotech/25.html (2000).*

7 *The Patent Act 35 U.S.C. §§ 101-103, 112 (2003).*

8 *Id.*

9 *See Diamond v. Chakrabarty, 447 U.S. 303, 309 (1980).*

10 *Parke-Davis & Co. v. H. K. Mulford & Co., 189 F. 95 (S.D.N.Y. 1911).*

11 *Id. at 97.*

12 *Id. at 103.*

13 *Funk Bros. Seed Co. v. Kalo Inoculant Co., 333 U.S. 127 (1948).*

14 *Id.*

15 *Id. at 129.*

16 *Id.*

17 *Chakrabarty, 447 U.S. at 305.*

18 *Id.*

19 *Id. at 309-10.*

20 *Id. at 310.*

21 *See Chakrabarty, 447 U.S. at 309.*

22 *Brendan Doherty, A Brief History of Biotechnology in Northern California, at http://www.bayareabioscience.org/historyofbiotech.pdf (n.d.).*

23 Ex Parte Allen, 2 U.S.P.Q.2d 1425 (Bd. Pat. App. & Interferences 1987).

24 Id.

25 Patent and Trademark Office Notice: Animals-Patentability, 1077 Official Gazette U.S. Pat. & Trademark Off. 8 (Apr. 21, 1987).

26 Id. at 127-28.

27 U.S. Patent No. 5,565,186 (issued October 15, 1996).

28 U.S. Patent No. 5,625,126 (issued April 29, 1997).

29 See Chakrabarty, 447 U.S. at 309.

30 35 U.S.C. § 103(a).

31 § 103(b).

32 Id.

33 See In re Deuel, 51 F.3d 1552 (Fed. Cir. 1995).

34 Id. at 1555-56.

35 Id.

36 Id. at 1558-59.

37 Id. at 1558.

38 John M. Golden, Biotechnology, Technology Policy, and Patentability: Natural Products and Inventions in the American System, 50 Emory L.J. 101, 119-22 (2001).

39 See Doherty, supra note 20.

40 35 U.S.C. ßß 200-212.

41 Id.

42 ß 200.

43 See Golden, supra note 37.

44 American Association for the Advancement of Science, Research, Innovation, and Patents, Science and Technology in Congress (May 2002), at http://www.aaas.org/spp/cstc/stc/stc/02/02-05/patents.htm.

45 Id.

46 Id.

47 Stanford University Medical Center Office of Technology Licensing, Fact File, at http://www.med.stanford.edu/shs/update/archives/dec1998/fact.html (1998).

48 Lisa Raines, Understanding the Hatch-Waxman Act: Biotechnology and Patent Term Extension Issues, 54 Food Drug L.J. 237 (1999).

49 Id.

50 Id.

51 35 U.S.C. ßß 155-156.

52 Intermedics, Inc. v. Ventritex, Inc., 775 F. Supp. 1269, 1276 (N.D. Cal. 1991) (discussing the legislative history of the Act).

53 Id.

54 35 U.S.C. ß 103(c).

55 See Eric K. Steffe, et al., Biotech Collaborations and Maximizing Patent Protection: Two Hypotheticals, 27 AIPLA Q.J. 149, 169-72 (1999).

56 Id. at 169-70.

57 Daniel S. Levine, "Biotech Industry Edges Closer to Stem-Cell Research," San Francisco Business Times, at http://www.bizjournals.com/sanfrancisco/stories/2003/05/12/story3.html?jst=s_rs_hl (May 12, 2003).

58 Id.

59 The USPTO class codes searched were 23, 71, 75, 95, 95, 106, 204, 205, 208, 210, 260, 423, 424, 435, 436, 502, 504, 514, 518, 520, 521, 528, 530, 532, 536, 540, 544, 546, 548, 552, 554, 556, 558, 560, 562, 564, 568, 585, 588, 623, 800, 930, 987.

CHAPTER SEVEN
FUTURE OF GENOMIC REVOLUTION

Article reprinted from The BioChemist 25 (2) pp. 30-34 © The BioChemical Society.